"To be completely free one must
become a slave to a set of laws"
Cicero

Dear reader,
Your life is a work of art,
which you haven't worked
on especially hard so far.
This book will remedy that,
providing you with the
tools to sculpt your base
clay into a masterpiece of
creative self-expression.
Follow the Diary's weekly
tasks in your own inimitable
fashion, documenting the
results as you go along,
and the year 2009 will be
guaranteed to stand out
when your life flashes past
you in the final split second
before death! Good luck.

Ben

Henrik

Benrik are Ben Carey and Henrik Delehag, authors of This Diary Will Change Your Life and other books in a similar inspirational vein. Their aim is to twist everyday reality into a more pleasing shape than that currently on offer. New readers are invited to follow the Diary's tasks online at www.benrik.co.uk, along with the other devotees.

Personal details

(fill in the gaps as you go along)

Name..

....

Address...

Date of birth...

Home phone number.....................................

Mobile phone number...................................

Email address...

Claim to fame...

Claim to genius.......................................

Year you will be discovered by the world..................

Before death ☐ After death ☐

Novels published......................................

Works of art exhibited................................

Films distributed.....................................

Nobel prizes won......................................

Hearts broken...

Magazine covers.......................................

Awards..

Honorary professorships...............................

Citations in academic literature......................

Retrospectives of your work...........................

Biographies of you....................................

Time "Man/Woman of the year 2009"? Yes ☐ No ☐

Affix photos of yourself as you change throughout the year.

January	February	March
April	May	June
July	August	September
October	November	December

2009 Schedule

1	Make an entirely new "New Year Resolution"	☐
2	Open a home restaurant	☐
3	Subvert consumer society from within	☐
4	Recruit a celebrity to the Benrik cult	☐
5	Swearing Week	☐
6	Find suspicious activity and report it	☐
7	Extreme Valentine Week	☐
8	Hand out a calling card to strangers this week	☐
9	Mutiny Week: Rise up against your leaders	☐
10	Secret Admirer Week	☐
11	Protest against everything	☐
12	Grant someone three wishes	☐
13	Eat wrong	☐
14	Spring clean the streets	☐
15	Taliban Week: Impose your values on everyone else	☐
16	Everything has a price: Find out what it is	☐
17	Apply to your secret service	☐
18	Follow opposite gender magazines' instructions	☐
19	No Small Talk Week	☐
20	"Who's Who" Week: Apply for inclusion	☐
21	Rat Race Week: Be ultra-competitive	☐
22	"Change one life" Week	☐
23	Treat people according to how much money they have	☐
24	Window Art Week	☐
25	Share your every thought with others	☐
26	Blackmail someone on the internet	☐

Tick each task as you accomplish it.

27	Epidemic Week: Everyone develop a mystery illness	☐
28	Benrik Charter Flight Week: Go on holiday together	☐
29	Insider Trading Week	☐
30	Ugly Week: Uglify yourself	☐
31	Squatting Week	☐
32	Embrace marketing	☐
33	"Cheers" Week	☐
34	"Manana Manana" Week: Slow society down	☐
35	Lifelong Education Week	☐
36	Hire a prostitute for a non-sexual purpose	☐
37	Positive Spamming Week	☐
38	Open yourself up to criticism	☐
39	Communism Week	☐
40	Godfather Week	☐
41	Synchronize society's watches	☐
42	Live beyond your means	☐
43	Foot Fetish Week	☐
44	Benrik Babysitting Week: Reprogramme a child	☐
45	Make a suggestion to a billionaire	☐
46	Dig your own grave	☐
47	Non-verbal Communication Week	☐
48	Make friends with an insect	☐
49	Let Benrik track your location via your mobile phone	☐
50	Closure Week	☐
51	Save the planet at any cost	☐
52	Send anonymous Christmas presents	☐

Make a New Year Resolution that no one in history has ever made before

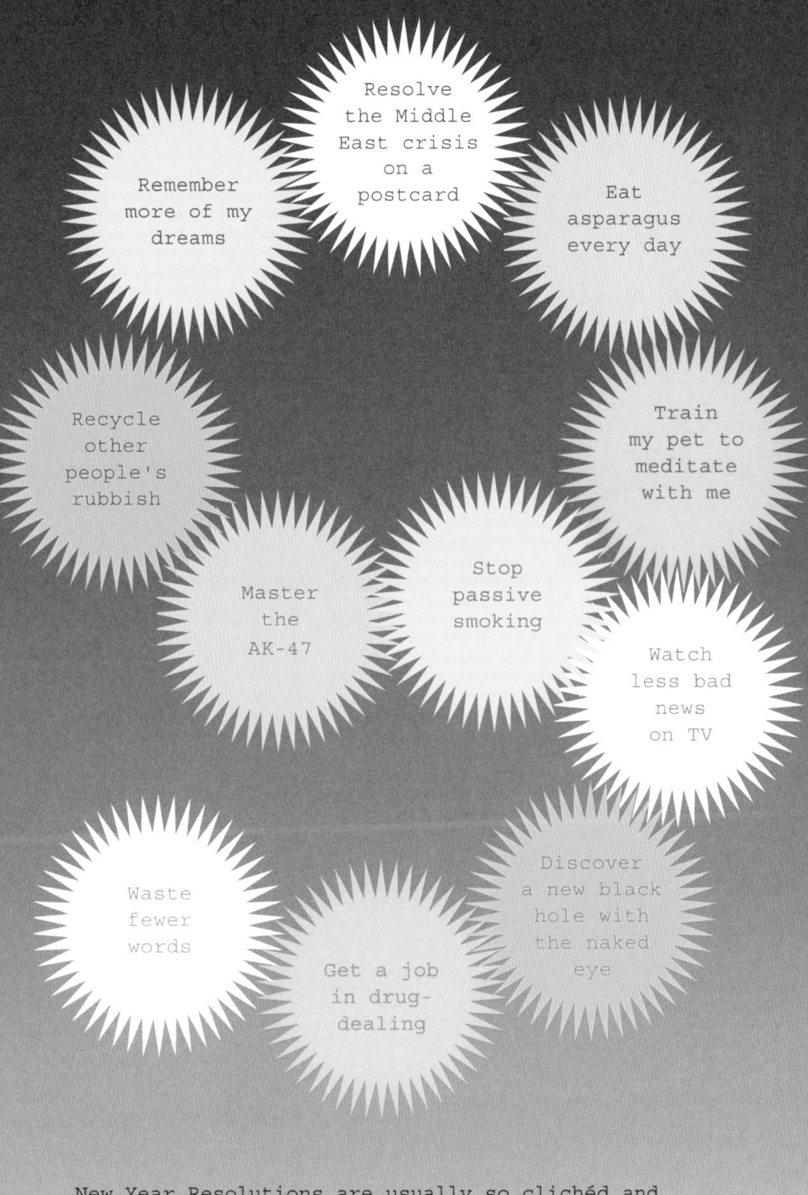

New Year Resolutions are usually so clichéd and unimaginative, it's no wonder they're not kept. This year, come up with your very own unique resolution, and you'll be more likely to follow it through.

Monday 29

Tuesday 30

Wednesday 31

Thursday 1

Friday 2

Saturday 3

Sunday 4

Monday 5

Tuesday 6

Wednesday 7

Thursday 8

Friday 9

Saturday 10

Sunday 11

This week:
open a home
restaurant

Ted and Linda Biggins

are pleased to welcome you
for one week only at our
exclusive restaurant situated

Opposite the Esso garage, the High Street,

for some delicious home cooking
and friendly service.

Please call 020 7947 451
for reservations

One of the few positive outcomes of Cuba's faltering economy is that hundreds of restaurants have opened up in people's private homes. Known as palabres, they allow you to eat food that is usually much better than that found in the official restaurants.

Menu

Starter

Soup à la Biggins

Mains

Ted and Linda's home-baked special

Dessert

Chef's delight

£ 14.95 for two courses

£ 18.95 for three courses

Download this advertising template at www.benrik.co.uk

This week, open up your living room to the crowds for a taste of your home cooking. Write a menu using the template above, post it around your neighbourhood, and start taking bookings. How to set the prices: Standard restaurant profit margins are close to 70%. So multiply the cost of the ingredients by 3 and simply divide it by the number of diners.

This week, subvert consumer society from within

Visit luxury stores, pretend to examine their goods and use the opportunity to hide these messages inside for the eventual buyers to discover.

This bag will never make up for your loveless childhood...

Has this purchase made you feel better about yourself?

This vase is expensive yet empty - same as you?

Imagine how many families you could feed for the price of this item.

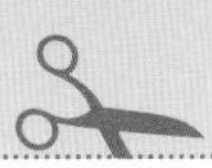

With this boot,
you are crushing
the poor.

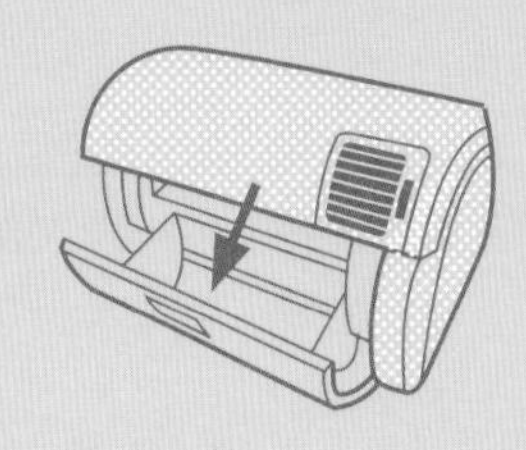

Congratulations
for buying a car.
Well done you!

Have you read
much Marx lately,
you capitalist
swine?

Happy?
I didn't think so…

Monday 12

Tuesday 13

Wednesday 14

Thursday 15

Friday 16

Saturday 17

Sunday 18

Monday 19

Tuesday 20

Wednesday 21

Thursday 22

Friday 23

Saturday 24

Sunday 25

Recruit a celebrity to the Benrik cult this week

Tom Cruise has done wonders for Scientology, advocating it in public and helping it reach a younger, trendier audience. Benrik too require a celebrity to join their "extreme life-changing" cause and boost their profile. This week, every reader must try and convert a celebrity to Benrik, by filling in the page opposite, bookmarking it, and sending this Diary to a famous person of their choice. Anyone who gets a genuine reply will feature in Benrik's Hall Of Fame (unless the reply takes legal form).

To the celebrity receiving this Diary: to promote the "extreme life-change" cause, please hold the book in the following way as you enter or leave celebrity parties.

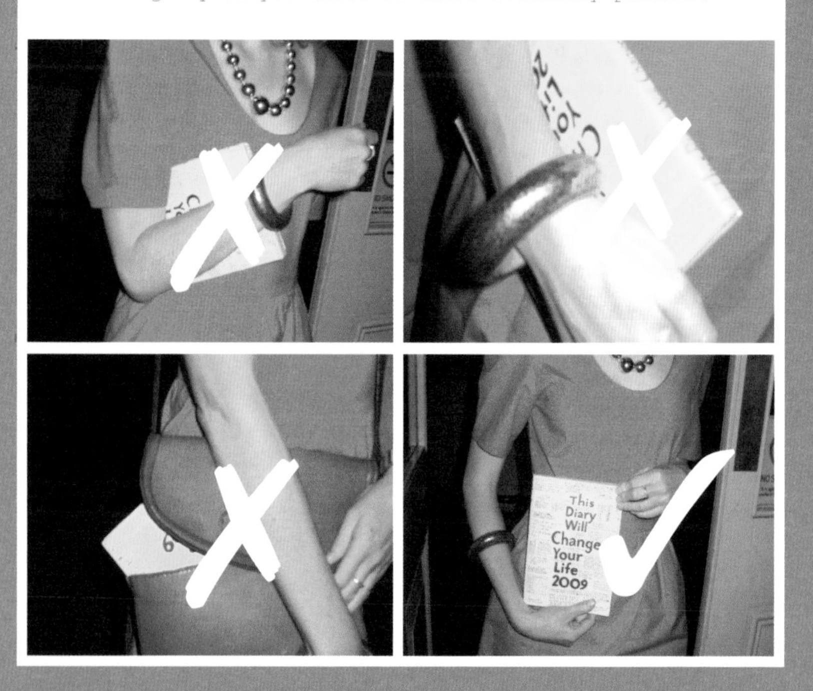

Dear Celebrity name

I have long admired your work, and in particular

Relevant work detail e.g. film part, hit song, lengthy novel

which just blew me away on so many levels, like

Name one level on which you were especially blown away

I'm no one in particular, just a Job title

from Location . But I thought I'd send you this book. It's none of my business really, but I read in the press recently that you had problems because of

Give details of recent tabloid story concerning the celebrity

They obviously make all this up, but still, it sounds like you could use a radical life-change. Follow this diary's instructions every week and you'll get much more positive publicity let me assure you! Anyway, I don't want to bother you any longer, as I have my own problems Name a few of your problems

I urge you to visit www.benrik.co.uk and join us for your own sake. Good luck.

Sign here

P.S. Call me on Your mobile phone number if you need to discuss.

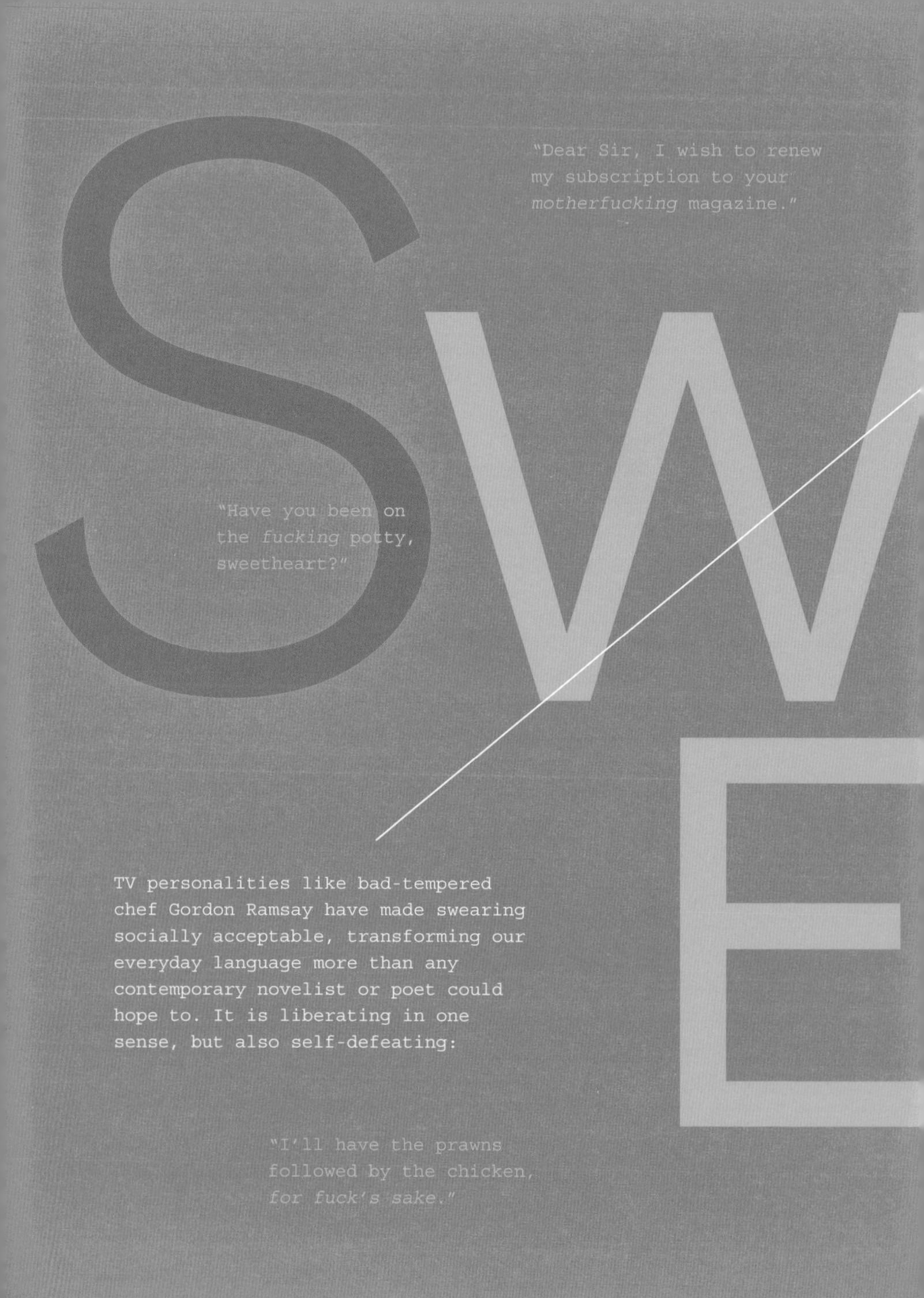

TV personalities like bad-tempered chef Gordon Ramsay have made swearing socially acceptable, transforming our everyday language more than any contemporary novelist or poet could hope to. It is liberating in one sense, but also self-defeating:

If we swear constantly, is it still swearing?

Ear K

"*Fuck* me, that cappuccino was delicious, thanks."

"Who's a good kitty-*fucking*-kat?"

"Will you *shitting* marry me?"

"Dear *wanker*, I am writing to apply for an extension to my overdraft."

Test the boundaries of this new world this week by swearing in every sentence you write or utter, and monitoring the reaction.

Don't use the word "cunt" though, which is like a powerful antibiotic of last resort – when it loses its effectiveness, humanity will have run out of swearing resources and swearing will come to an end.

Monday 26

Tuesday 27

Wednesday 28

Thursday 29

Friday 30

Saturday 31

Sunday 1

Monday 2

Tuesday 3

Wednesday 4

Thursday 5

Friday 6

Saturday 7

Sunday 8

IMPORTANT! Book your summer holiday now in accordance with the instructions for week 28!

This week: find suspicious activity and report it

We must be vigilant in the face of the terrorist threat. As the UK police suggests, "where there's unusual activity that doesn't fit normal day-to-day life, we need to know" – a broad call to action if ever there was one. Still, citizens must do their duty: "if you suspect it, report it". Examples of suspicious activity:

confidential anti-terrorist hotline:

0800 789 321

st photos of the suspicious activity on www.benrik.co.uk

"Mary at 29a hasn't put her recycling box out this week."

"There's a chap outside my house who's been tying his shoelace for two whole minutes."

"This bald man in my local Tesco's just bought a three-pack of shampoo."

"The Johnsons have bought fertiliser and it's not even planting season."

"A dark brown 4x4
has just driven past
the train station
three times."

"My colleague always
puts the phone down
when I walk in."

"The curtains at No 98
are always closed in
the afternoon."

"How can that ghastly
family afford such a bigger
house than ours?"

Extreme Valentine Week:

DOUBLECHECK YOUR PARTNER ISN'T CHEATING

"All is fair in love and war" was surely coined with the internet age in mind. This Valentine's Day, make sure your love is true - using the latest in unobtrusive electronic surveillance technology.

CHECK THEIR EMAILS
Look out for: emails in folders with deliberately boring names such as "tax issues" or "pilates appointments"

FIT THEIR CAR WITH A GPS TRACKER
Look out for: regular parking in unfamiliar residential neighbourhoods

MONITOR THEIR MOBILE-PHONE BILL
Look out for: regular calls to unknown number at the time they walk the dog or you take a shower

INSTALL KEYSTROKE-LOGGING SOFTWARE ON THEIR PC
Look out for: keystrokes that form the words "sex", "meet", "gagging", "motel" or "divorce"

OLD-SCHOOL: LISTEN TO ANYTHING THEY SAY IN THEIR SLEEP
Look out for: soft moaning of someone else's name

True love confirmed ☐ True love cancelled ☐

Monday 9

Tuesday 10

Wednesday 11

Thursday 12

Friday 13

Saturday 14

Sunday 15

Monday 16

Tuesday 17

Wednesday 18

Thursday 19

Friday 20

Saturday 21

Sunday 22

Hand out a calling card to strangers this week

The calling card is the ancestor of the more mundane business card, and was used by the Chinese and European nobilities to lubricate social interaction. Aristocrats would leave calling cards at each other's homes - and if the gesture was reciprocated, they would visit each other. Our times cry out for an updated version. The "Benrik Calling Card" is to be handed out to intriguing strangers, whom one suspects might enhance one's life. They are tailored to modern urban interaction, and should be dispensed with a silent smile, putting the onus on the receiver to get in touch. Here are a few examples from the range - duplicate them yourself, or purchase the finished article via www.thiswebsitewillchangeyourlife.com in partnership with Moo.com.

You look nice.
Get in touch
sometime!

I loved the book
you're reading. Call
when you've finished
it and let me know
what you thought!

If you ever break up with your partner, here's my number:

....

I DON'T KNOW YOU BUT I WISH YOU WELL IN YOUR LIFE!

SMILE!

IT MIGHT NEVER HAPPEN.

I commute on this tube line too. Next time, let's talk!

MUTINY WEEK! THIS WEEK, RISE UP AGAINST YOUR LEADERS!

1. Marketing decisions to be taken by collective vote!

2. All memos declared null and void!

3. All meetings cancelled with immediate effect!

4. Burn all P45 forms!

5. Recall all products!

Do not be fooled. The soporific nature of the modern workplace is a trap, designed to cover up its inequitable power structure: even though they pay you token wages, your bosses still exploit you, making vast corporate profits off the back of your labour and broken middle-class dreams. This week, enough is enough! Conspire with others in your organisation and mutiny: refuse to obey orders, and establish a new power structure. Post these around the workplace to kickstart the mutiny.

6.
Suspend
Share
price!

7.
CEO to be
locked in
stationery
cupboard!

8.
Anarchy
YES!
Hierarchy
NO!

9.
Immediate
inflation-
adjusted
pay rises!

10.
Call bank
and initiate
merger with
other mutinous
firms!

Monday 23

Tuesday 24

Wednesday 25

Thursday 26

Friday 27

Saturday 28

Sunday 1

Monday 2

Tuesday 3

Wednesday 4

Thursday 5

Friday 6

Saturday 7

Sunday 8

Promote a friend that you think everyone should know about.

Some people are just so radiant that everyone should know them. If you're lucky enough to know such a person yourself, share your luck with others this week, and advertise them to the world!

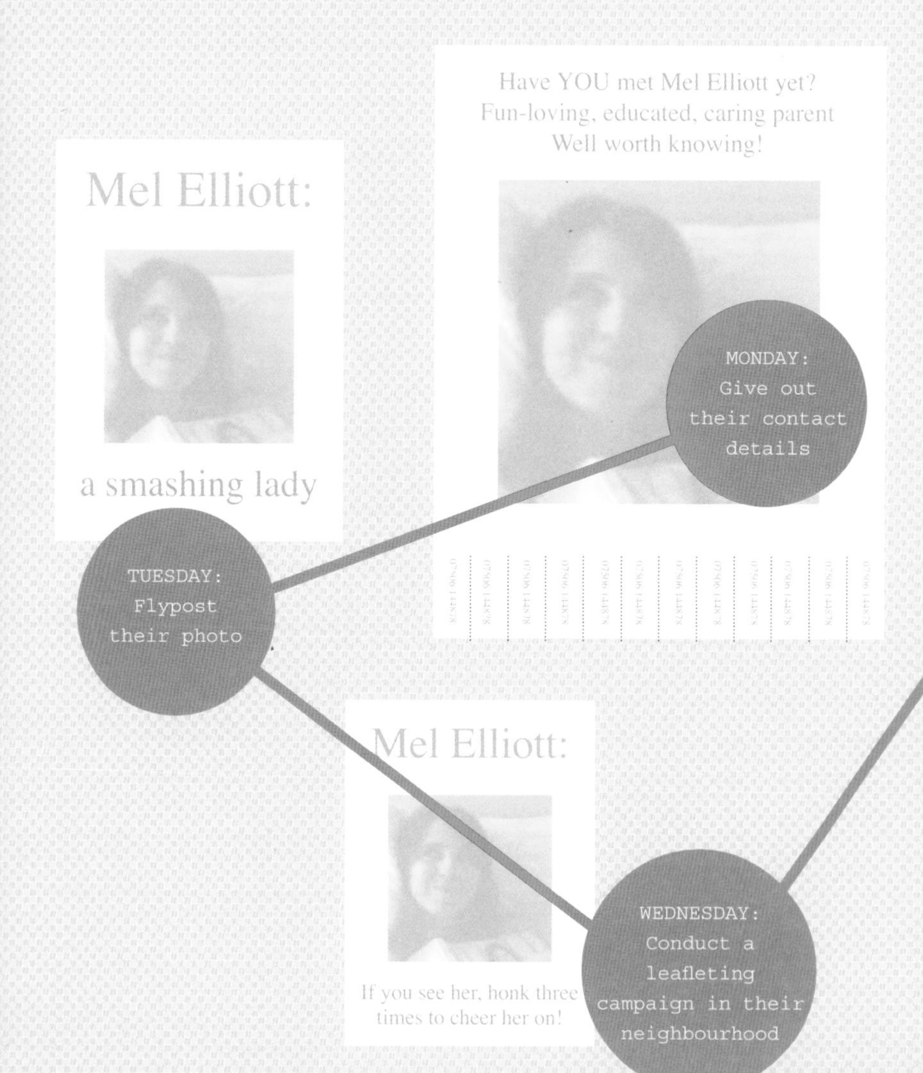

"...she's just been through so much, Brian, and I think she's kept her dignity, hasn't she? That's the Mel Elliott I know, always smiling! And I'll tell you something else about her..."

THURSDAY:
Call radio chat shows about them

Mel Elliott
Unofficial
Fan Site!!!

Register here for updates on Mel's life

Click here for Mel's home address

FRIDAY:
Set up a website

Mel Elliott, Tower Hamlets, London
to receive CBE for her works.

Name	Address	Signature

SATURDAY:
Petition for them to be honoured

Press release 08-03-09

Mel Elliott Latest News
For immediate release Today

Mel Elliott made five people's day by noticing them. Charismatic Mel said: "If I can spread a little happiness, and it doesn't cost me anything, then why wouldn't I?" A mystery campaign by a secret admirer this week has drawn Mel to public attention, culminating in an appearance on *Newsnight* on Friday night, where Jeremy Paxman gave her a big hug. Experts say

SUNDAY:
Send out a press release

THIS WEEK, PROTEST

Here are some protest templates which you may download from www.thiswebsitewillchangeyourlife.com and fill in according to the topic you are protesting about

DOWN WITH .... !	STOP THE .... !	FREE .... !
WHAT DO WE WANT? .... ! WHEN DO WE WANT IT? .... !	NO TO .... !	SAVE THE .... !

Protesting was much easier in the 80s, when apartheid provided an unambiguous focus for moral outrage. These days, there are thousands of causes that clamour for our attention, with no clear front-runner.

AGAINST EVERYTHING

WE WANT .... !	.... MUST RESIGN!	NO MORE .... !
BAN .... IMMED-IATELY!	.... =MUR-DERER!	WE DEMAND .... !

The solution is not to be paralysed into apathy, but to protest against everything going. This week, consult the internet for protests in your area and participate in one a day (www.protest.net).

Monday 9

Tuesday 10

Wednesday 11

Thursday 12

Friday 13

Saturday 14

Sunday 15

Monday 16

Tuesday 17

Wednesday 18

Thursday 19

Friday 20

Saturday 21

Sunday 22

Grant someone 3 wishes

Be your very own genie: pick an acquaintance or a stranger at random and offer to make three of their desires come true this week. Be sure to impose these minor caveats before they get too carried away though:

1) No supernatural wishes, unless you are a genuine djinn.

2) No overtly sexual wishes, although there is probably a market for that kind of thing.

3) Nothing murderous, unless the victim really deserves it.

Nice achievable wishes to suggest might include: "I wish my fence were repainted overnight", "I wish I had a puppy!" or "I wish my wife knew how much I loved her"

Wish 1: ....
....
....
....
....
....
....
....
Deadline: .... /.......... /.......... Budget: ....
Completed: Yes [] No []

Wish 2: ....
....
....
....
....
....
....
....
Deadline: .... /.......... /.......... Budget: ....
Completed: Yes [] No []

Wish 3: ....
....
....
....
....
....
....
....
Deadline: .... /.......... /.......... Budget: ....
Completed: Yes [] No []

THIS WEEK, EAT WRONG

Modern health experts keep issuing contradictory advice. One week, wine is good for you. The next, vitamins are out. This week, eat the opposite of whatever you're told to. You'll enjoy yourself more and you may well be proved right in the long-run anyway.

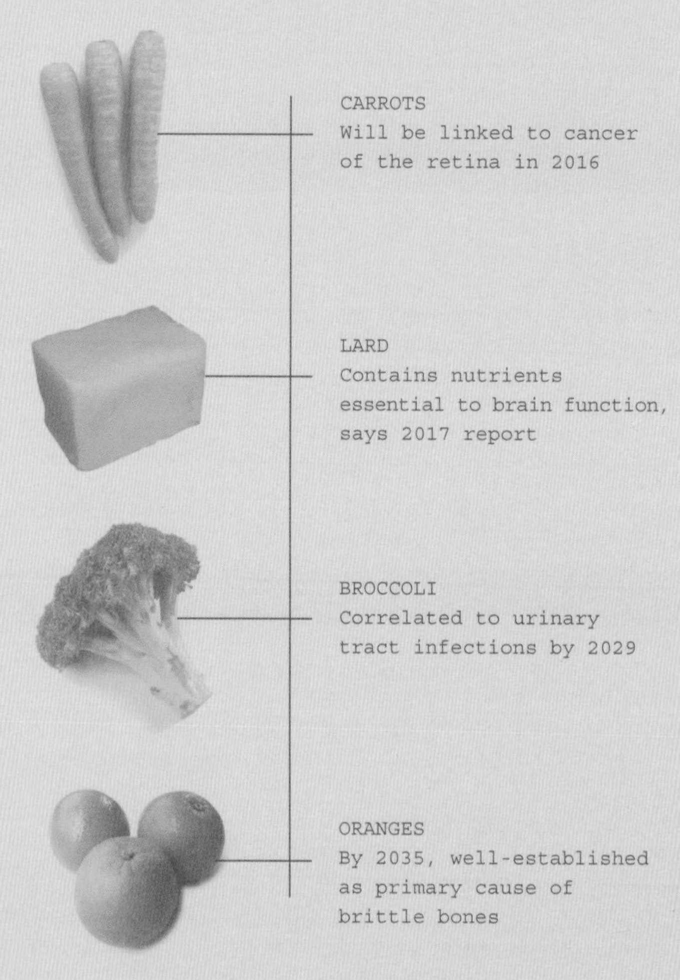

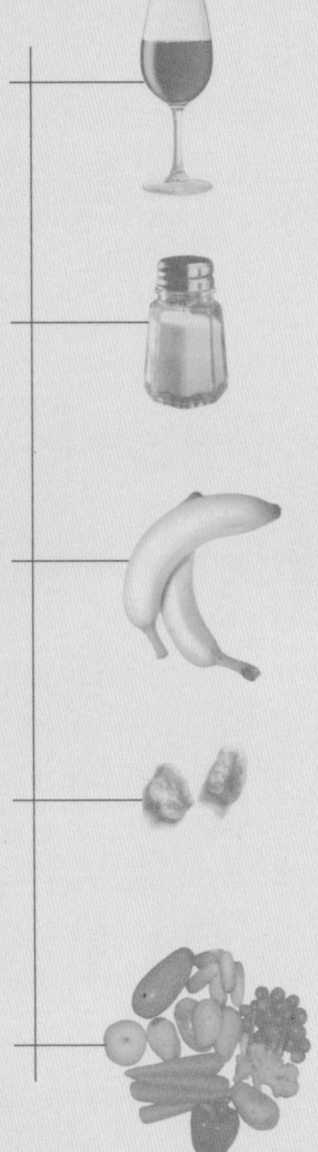

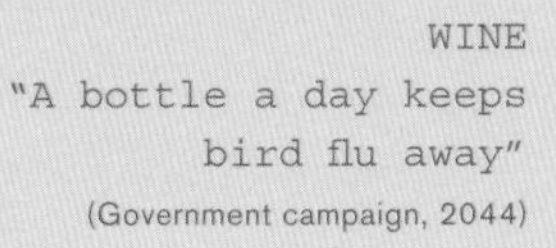

WINE
"A bottle a day keeps
bird flu away"
(Government campaign, 2044)

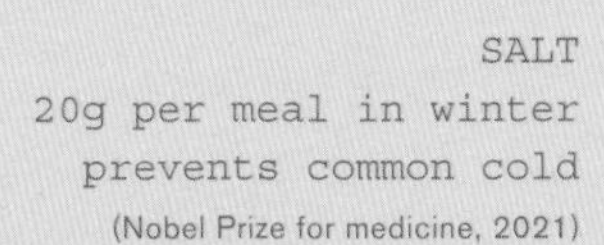

SALT
20g per meal in winter
prevents common cold
(Nobel Prize for medicine, 2021)

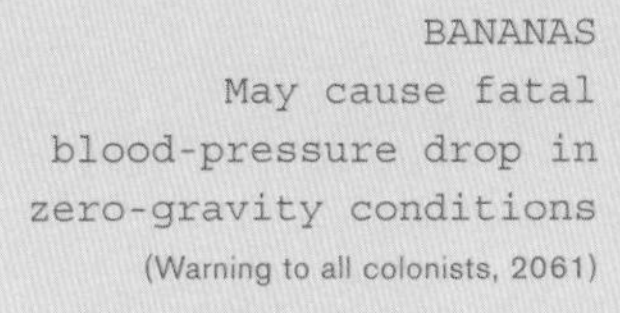

BANANAS
May cause fatal
blood-pressure drop in
zero-gravity conditions
(Warning to all colonists, 2061)

PORK SCRATCHINGS
In combination with avocado
purée, increase longevity
by up to 8 years
(The Lancet, 2030)

FRUIT & VEGETABLES
"Discredited five-a-day
policy responsible for
agonizing haemorrhagic
deaths of millions"
(BBC headline, June 2050)

Monday 23

Tuesday 24

Wednesday 25

Thursday 26

Friday 27

Saturday 28

Sunday 29

Monday 30

Tuesday 31

Wednesday 1

Thursday 2

Friday 3

Saturday 4

Sunday 5

This week, spring clean the streets

The streets are filthy! This week, everyone must deep-clean the patch in front of their house and then take care to keep it pristine.

GRAFFITI

Spray with solvents containing monoglycol ethers and glycol acetates, leave for ten minutes, then wipe off clean.

CHEWING GUM

If it is under a week old, try scraping it off with a sharp knife. Otherwise, use a high-powered jet-blast machine (3000psi/200 bar minimum).

WEEDS

Remove visible weeds, then fill gaps between blocks with sand containing slow-release herbicide to prevent further infestation.

DIRT AND GRIME

Remove with a hot steam wash (water flow rate l/h 500-960), scrubbing any leftovers with an industrial wire brush.

URINE STAINS

Apply two-to-one dilution of liquid bleach, then rub with scouring powder using steel wool 000 grade and mineral spirits.

BIRD DROPPINGS

Scrape off carefully with a wooden spatula, taking care not to breathe in any of the dust. Then use a hydrofluoric acid-based solution. Do not use bleach, as it may react with the ammonia in the droppings, releasing toxic gases!

TALIBAN WEEK: IMPOSE YOUR VALUES ON EVERYONE ELSE

The decline of shared moral values is undermining our society. This week, try to bring back a little cohesion by enforcing your personal morality on those around you. Don't be afraid to coerce people a little to help them internalize your values. They may protest, but remind them - it's for their own good. Here are a few methods, developed by experts in the field.

PICKET THEM

DAUB DISAPPROVING
COMMENTS ON THEIR HOUSES

NAME AND SHAME THEM

BURY THEM IN THE GROUND
AND STONE THEM TO DEATH

Monday 6

Tuesday 7

Wednesday 8

Thursday 9

Friday 10

Saturday 11

Sunday 12

Monday 13

Tuesday 14

Wednesday 15

Thursday 16

Friday 17

Saturday 18

Sunday 19

Everything has a price: this week, find out what it is

Selling you their
unfinished coffee: £5

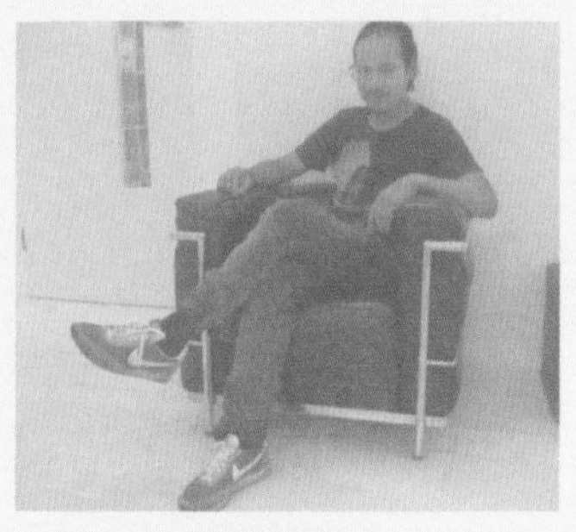

Selling you their
left sock: £9

Selling you a mouthful
of their three-course
lunch: £6

Selling you the
book they're reading:
Book price + £10

Go up to people and ask them how much they would require to part with their much-prized possessions, there and then. Here is a rough guide to the going rates.

Selling you their pet: £1200

Selling you their umbrella in a downpour: £35

Selling you their place in the queue: £15

Selling you their soul: Negotiable

Research sample: 481 people, 18–75, from June 12–16, 2008, London. Margin of error +- 6%

Apply to your secret service this week

Secret-service work is mostly tedious and mind-numbing; it involves sifting through mountains of contradictory data, and sitting through hours of cross-departmental meetings to decide who to invade based on the inconclusive results. The application process is the fun bit: will you get through the security clearance process, or will they discover something in your record that disqualifies you from joining? Here is the application form for MI6, the British secret service (technically correct name:

Contact details

Forenames.. Surname.. Title...................
Home Phone No................................ Work Phone No................................ Mobile Phone No................................
Permanent Residential Address..
Town/City.. Country (e.g. UK).. Postcode...........................
All other surnames used inc former married name(s)..
Place of birth.. Nationality (including dual nationality)..
Occupation:..
Home address including date moved into this address (month & year)..
....
Any other addresses in the last 10 years, including dates at each address:..
....
Current salary: £..Salary sought: £..
Where did you hear about this vacancy?...

Family details

If you have a partner or co-habitant, please complete the following details. If not then proceed to next section.
Surname now.. Surname at birth (if different from surname now).................................
Maiden name /any other surnames used:..
Full forenames:..Place of birth:......................................

Education

Please enter the names of schools, colleges and/or universities you have attended.
Secondary Education (School/Sixth Form..
Start Date.. End Date..
Higher Education (College/University):...
Start Date.. End Date..
Postgraduate Education:...
Start Date.. End Date..

Qualifications

Please input all the exams you have taken from GCSE upwards and the grades you were awarded, including fails and resits. For non-UK qualifications please give the original results, not the UK equivalents. You will be required to provide certificates to verify your education qualifications at a later stage.

Level	Type
....	....
....	....
....	....
....	....
....	....

Work experience

Please give full details of significant employment. Indicate whether it was full-time, part-time, vacation work or an industrial placement and provide details of specific responsibilities, experience and knowledge gained.
....
....
Please enter the name and address of your present employer. Please also provide details of your job title, dates of employment and a short description of your duties. If unemployed, please enter N/A.
....
.... What is your notice period?...
Please give details of any period since you left secondary school which is not already accounted for, including gap years and unemployment:
....

Secret Intelligence Service). The applications and background checks take six months to process, so report your success or failure back to Benrik by November. Or look up procedures in your country, which should be broadly similar, but may also involve arrest and torture if you fail. Good luck!

Didn't get in? Complain with a strongly-worded letter to the Director General of Security and Safety, Ministry of Defence, Level 6 Zone D, Main Building, Whitehall, London SW1A 2HB. If all else fails, apply to the French secret service, as they are less fussy about who they take on.

Language skills

Please enter details of your main spoken language and other language skills you have.

Language	Read	Speak	Write
....	....	....	....
....	....	....	....
....	....	....	....

Competency

The following questions relate to some of the interests and skills that are required to perform effectively in the role you have applied for. Please ensure that you give a specific example for each question, and that you answer all of the supplementary questions. Your answers should be no more than 250 words per question. To ensure you have provided enough information we would advise that you write a minimum of 200 words.

1 What attracts you to a career in intelligence and why do you think you would be suited to it?

....

....

2 What do you see as the major intelligence priorities for SIS in the next five years?

....

....

3 Give an example of a time when you had to respond to a change in environment or circumstances that changed unexpectedly.

....

....

4 Give an example of a team in which you take, or have taken part. Describe the role you played and how you contributed to the working of the team.

....

....

5 Describe a complex task or project, preferably outside of formal education, where you had to understand and interpret information from a variety of sources, draw conclusions and make an informed decision or recommendation.

....

....

6 Give a specific example of where you have convinced someone to do something which they would not have done without your intervention and comment on how you achieved this.

....

....

7 Please provide a pen portrait of yourself and your personal history.

....

....

8 Please outline your interests outside of work and study.

....

....

Guidelines

Security vetting is conducted by the Defence Vetting Agency (DVA), who will assess you for "long term, frequent and uncontrolled access to TOP SECRET information or assets... or in order to satisfy requirements for access to material originating from other countries and international organisations". Requirements: You must be a British national. You must be loyal, honest and reliable, and not be vulnerable to blackmail or bribery. You must not have used Class A drugs in the year prior to application. You must not have used Class B drugs in the six months prior to application. A criminal record does not necessarily preclude your employment.

Send to: SIS Human Resources, Vauxhall, London SW2, UK.

Monday 20

Tuesday 21

Wednesday 22

Thursday 23

Friday 24

Saturday 25

Sunday 26

Monday 27

Tuesday 28

Wednesday 29

Thursday 30

Friday 1

Saturday 2

Sunday 3

WOMEN:

THIS WEEK, FOLLOW MEN'S MAGAZINES' INSTRUCTIONS

Men and women are given very different lifestyle guidance from the media. This week, get in touch with your masculine side by following men's orders and see if your life improves as a result.

Build muscle now

Power workout tips from Navy Seals

Get a six-pack for summer

Bulk up fast!

Join the hunt for Babe of the Year!

The best EVER lunchtime workout

TRY OUR 101 TOP CHAT-UP LINES

23 instant builder muscle tips

Buy and read: *Maxim, GQ, Nuts, FHM, Men's Health*

MEN:
THIS WEEK, FOLLOW WOMEN'S MAGAZINES' INSTRUCTIONS
Men and women are given very different lifestyle guidance from the media. This week, get in touch with your feminine side by following women's orders and see if your life improves as a result.

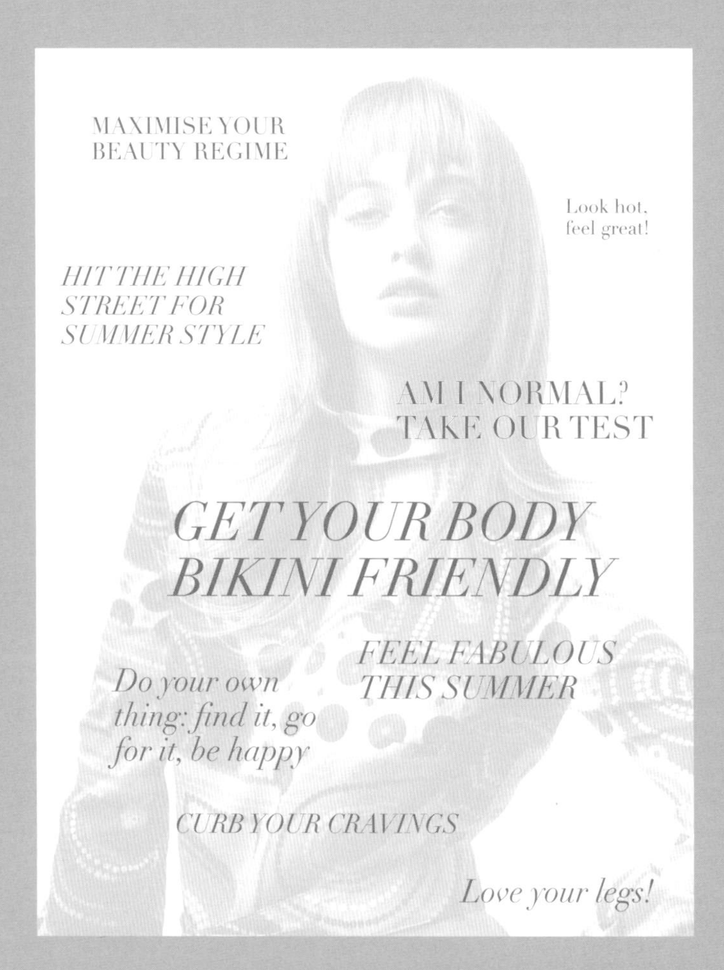

Buy and read: *Cosmo, Marie Claire, Grazia, Elle, Glamour*

NO SMALL TALK WEEK

Cut out the polite chitchat this week: save hours of your life + boost the country's economic productivity by millions! Forbidden expressions:
That's life I suppose
Well well well
How's your wife/husband /boyfriend/ girlfriend/ relative/pet
Hi
How are you
Lovely weather we're having

Monday 4

Tuesday 5

Wednesday 6

Thursday 7

Friday 8

Saturday 9

Sunday 10

Monday 11

Tuesday 12

Wednesday 13

Thursday 14

Friday 15

Saturday 16

Sunday 17

Who's Who Week

Apply for inclusion

Career

Education

Publications

Address

Family details

ANSTRUTHER, Dame Lydia Elizabeth, (Dame Lydia), DBE 2003 (CBE 1997); Chair, Commission for Social Equality for England and Wales, since 2007; *b* 10 March 1945; *d* of Michael John Anstruther and Nancy Elizabeth Anstruther (*née* Brownlee); *m* 1972, Dr Hugh Evans-Pritchard; two *s* two *d*. *Educ:* Magdalen College, Oxon. (BA Hons PPE 1967, MA 1970); Corpus Christi college, Cambridge Univ. (Bphil Social Research 1971). VSO India, 1972-74. Trainee researcher MRI, 1975-76; Sen. Res. Officer, then Chair, Malnutrition Working Gp, 1977-86; Chair, Norfolk / East Anglia NHS District Trust 1987-92; Dep. Chair, then Chair, Committee on Health Funding in subSaharan Africa 1990-2008. *Board memberships:* ICI, HSBC, Warburg. Hon. FRSH 2005; Hon. DLitt, Oxon. 2004. *Publications:* Halting epidemics successfully (A primer), 2002; Curing malaria, 2005. *Recreations:* playing bridge, writing verse, cross-country skiing. *Address:* Commission for Social Equality for England and Wales, 23 Whitehall, London SW1 5FT. *E-mail:* lydia.anstruther@socialequalitycommission.gsi.gov.uk.

Current entry

Who's Who lists the great and the good of this world, based on distinction and influence - as they put it, "a quality which singles them out from their fellows". As a Benrik reader, you are obviously an individual of talent and distinction who deserves such recognition. This week, nominate yourself for consideration by the *Who's Who* Selection Board: send a CV to nominations@ukwhoswho.com or post it to the Office of Who's Who, 38 Soho Square, London W1D 3HB. This is the format to follow, so you don't get turned down for the wrong reasons:

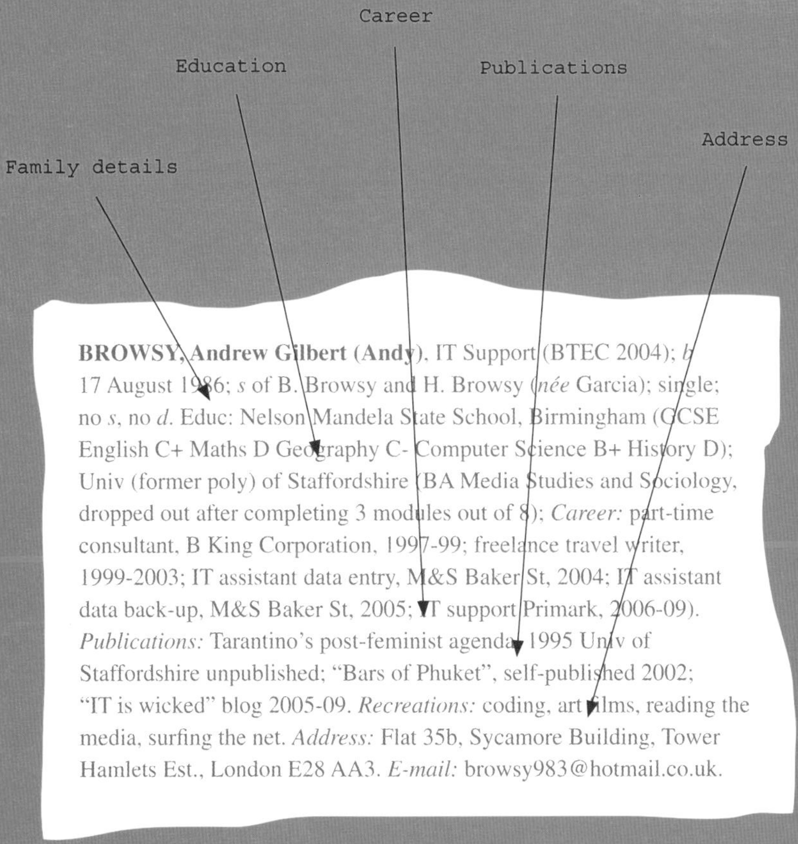

Career

Education

Publications

Address

Family details

BROWSY, Andrew Gilbert (Andy), IT Support (BTEC 2004); *b* 17 August 1986; *s* of B. Browsy and H. Browsy (*née* Garcia); single; no *s*, no *d*. Educ: Nelson Mandela State School, Birmingham (GCSE English C+ Maths D Geography C- Computer Science B+ History D); Univ (former poly) of Staffordshire (BA Media Studies and Sociology, dropped out after completing 3 modules out of 8); *Career:* part-time consultant, B King Corporation, 1997-99; freelance travel writer, 1999-2003; IT assistant data entry, M&S Baker St, 2004; IT assistant data back-up, M&S Baker St, 2005; IT support Primark, 2006-09). *Publications:* Tarantino's post-feminist agenda, 1995 Univ of Staffordshire unpublished; "Bars of Phuket", self-published 2002; "IT is wicked" blog 2005-09. *Recreations:* coding, art films, reading the media, surfing the net. *Address:* Flat 35b, Sycamore Building, Tower Hamlets Est., London E28 AA3. *E-mail:* browsy983@hotmail.co.uk.

Candidate entry

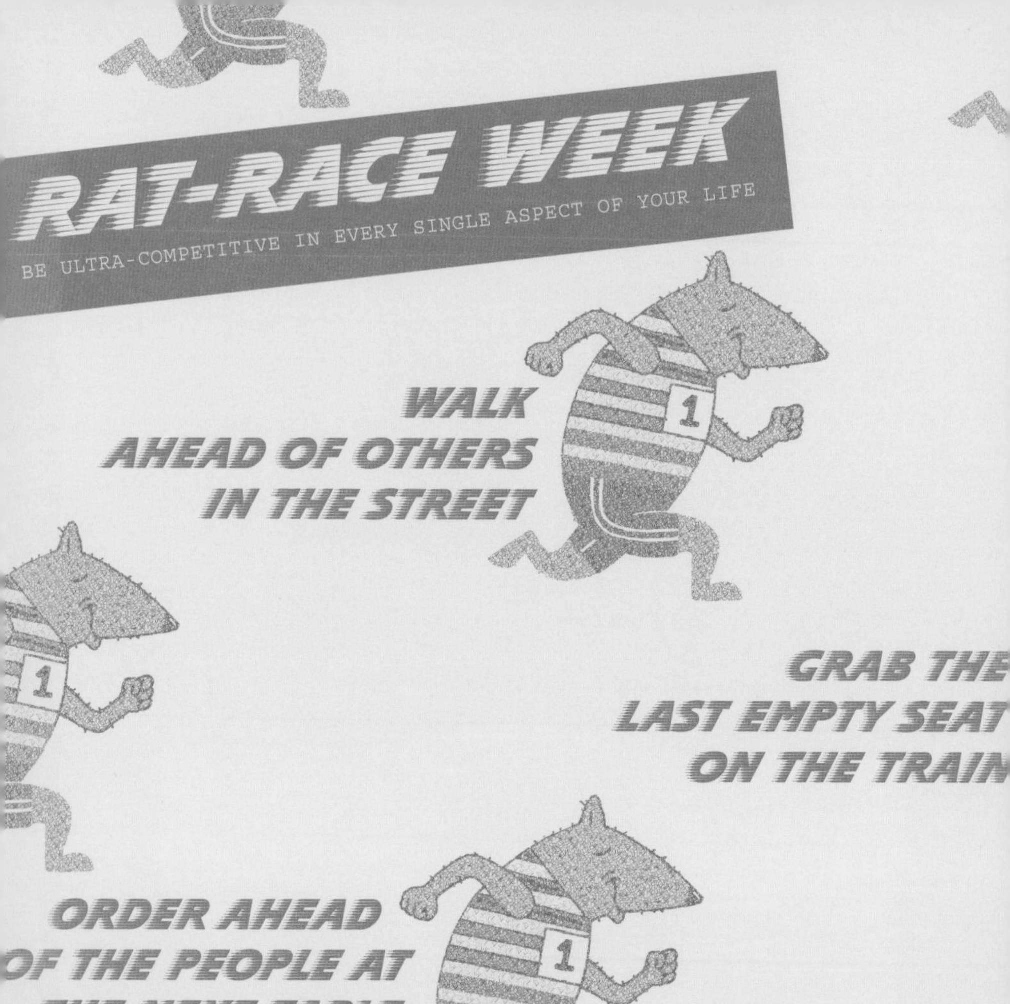
RAT-RACE WEEK
BE ULTRA-COMPETITIVE IN EVERY SINGLE ASPECT OF YOUR LIFE
WALK
AHEAD OF OTHERS
IN THE STREET
GRAB THE
LAST EMPTY SEAT
ON THE TRAIN
ORDER AHEAD
OF THE PEOPLE AT
THE NEXT TABLE

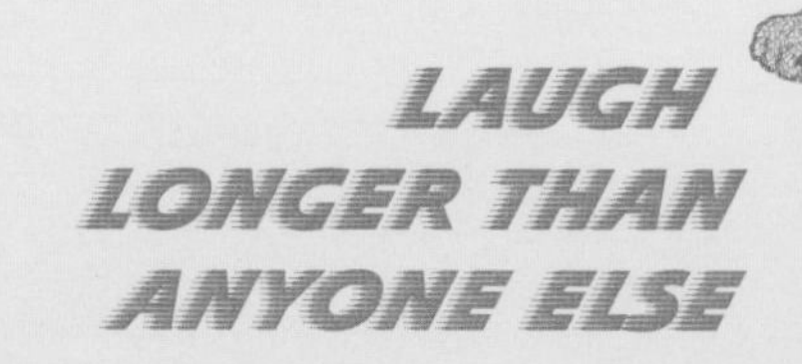
LAUGH
LONGER THAN
ANYONE ELSE

TAKE SOLE
CHARGE OF THE
REMOTE CONTROL
1
RECYCLE THE HIGHEST
PERCENTAGE
OF RUBBISH
1
1
PICK
THE FASTEST
QUEUE
1
TAKE UP MORE
OF THE BED THAN
YOUR PARTNER
1

Monday 18

Tuesday 19

Wednesday 20

Thursday 21

Friday 22

Saturday 23

Sunday 24

Monday 25

Tuesday 26

Wednesday 27

Thursday 28

Friday 29

Saturday 30

Sunday 31

"CHANGE ONE LIFE" WEEK

This week, all readers are to focus their energies on changing the life of one single lucky individual, picked at random by Benrik.

Volunteer: Apply by Monday 6p.m. GMT by emailing contact@benrik.co.uk with your details and a brief description of your life so far, and what needs changing in your opinion. Benrik do not guarantee that any life-change will be in accordance (or even remotely connected) with your wishes. If there are no suitable candidates, Benrik reserve the right to pick a volunteer directly.

This week, treat people according to how much money they have

	Name of person	Estimated annual income	Time spent in their company	Laughs at their jokes	Compliments on their good taste
Rich	Example:	£250,000	>10 hours	30+	"Your new wife is much cuter."
Middle class	Example:	£35,000	5 hours	10	"Those socks really suit you."
Poor	Example:	£10,000	<1 hour	0	"You don't smell too bad for a student."

Wealth dictates our social hierarchy, so let's embrace it this week: work out roughly what everyone you meet or know is worth, and behave accordingly. Here are some guidelines and a handy table to help you.

Conversational gambit	Favour to ask
"That's the funniest anecdote I've ever heard in my life! Tell it again!"	"Zurich have messed up my account. You couldn't spare £20,000 for a few weeks old boy?"
"What mortgage rate are you on?"	"How embarrassing, I've left my wallet at home. If you get this, I'll take you out next time."
"Have you got a job yet?"	"Stop calling me."

Monday 1

Tuesday 2

Wednesday 3

Thursday 4

Friday 5

Saturday 6

Sunday 7

Monday 8

Tuesday 9

Wednesday 10

Thursday 11

Friday 12

Saturday 13

Sunday 14

HELP!
I'M BEING
HELD
AGAINST
MY WILL!

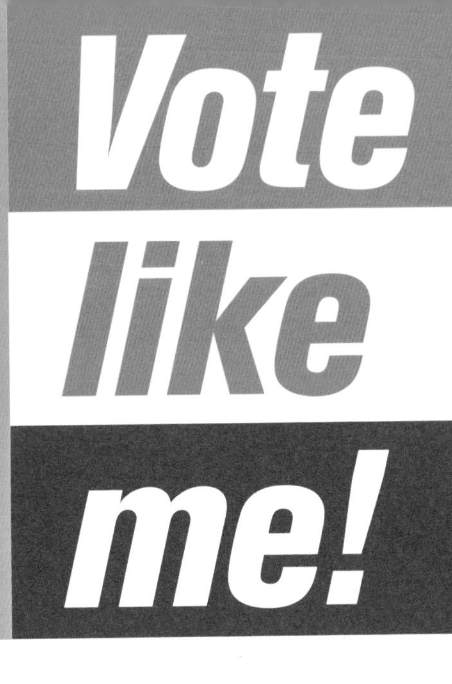

Window Art Week

I'm
fantasizing
about
you from
behind
these
blinds

I'm
lonely
in here,
there's
nothing
on TV

The key is under the mat

I'm not coming out until my demands are met

People feel a strange urge to display their tedious political views in their windows, when there are so many more interesting statements to make. This week, display your message to the world in your most prominent window, and see how the world responds. Here are a few examples to inspire you.

THIS FLAT IS WORTH £450,000, YOU LOSERS!

I dare you to burgle me, passer-by

THIS WEEK, SHARE YOUR EVERY THOUGHT WITH OTHERS

You are an extraordinary human being. The only reason others don't always appreciate this is because they're not inside your head to witness the creative maelstrom of your consciousness. This week, turn to the person nearest to you every time you think a thought, share it with them, and watch them succumb to the magnetic pull of your mind. If there is no one around, email or call. But get those precious thoughts out there!

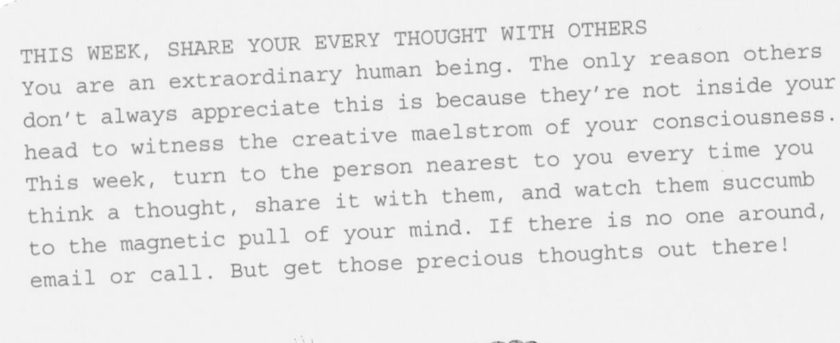

Week 25
One day they'll be able to stitch tiny mobile phones into our ears.
My wife doesn't understand me.
hat's my mother's
vourite colour? We've
ver discussed it.
That man is sweating like a pig.
I'm bloody starving.

Monday 15

Tuesday 16

Wednesday 17

Thursday 18

Friday 19

Saturday 20

Sunday 21

Monday 22

Tuesday 23

Wednesday 24

Thursday 25

Friday 26

Saturday 27

Sunday 28

Dear "Scoobster51"
In the future, your admission on the website "MySpace" that your hobbies include "pills, pills and more pills fookin' love it!!!" may handicap your employment prospects. I advise you to delete the reference, but don't worry, I have a screenshot which I will keep secure for you for a mere £15 a year.

THIS WEEK, BLACKMAIL SOMEONE ON THE INTERNET

Dear Sophie
I enjoyed reading your blog, in which you refer to your mother as "the bitch" and to your father as "the eunuch", for comic effect. I feel they would appreciate the joke and therefore propose to drop them a line about this via your school, Abingdon Girls Secondary, 56 Crown Road. Would you mind?

Hello Shelly
I was browsing the internet when I came across this rather revealing photograph of you, posted by your former boyfriend "Matt". It is a sad day when those we trust with such intimate moments betray us. Meanwhile, I wonder if your current husband "Andrew" should see it? £50 says no.

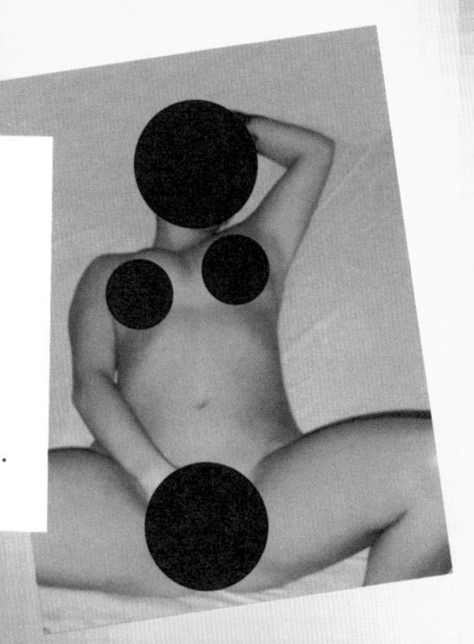

Social networking allows everyone to share their most personal details with complete strangers. As the media regularly point out, this is imprudent. Someone somewhere is no doubt harvesting drunken and sexual antics with a view to blackmailing their authors twenty years from now when they've become MPs or judges. You should not wait. This week, trawl social networks for incriminating self-disclosure, and scare those responsible into being less naïve.

Good morning,
Are you both Phil Barton, IT support manager for Vistos Financial Software Limited, and Phil998, busy member of the vibrant community on doggingsoutheast.co.uk (some of the photos are out of focus, but the beard is unmistakeable). Let's talk!

NB No blackmailing of fellow Benrik readers! That would be too easy.

Epidemic Week:

This week, everyone report to their local hospital with the same mystery illness

Following the SARS, BSE and bird flu scares, national health systems are now geared towards detecting patterns of illness early, in order to limit their spread. This week, test national readiness by collectively reporting to your nearest hospital A&E with the symptoms opposite. If the prevention systems are working, the nation should be under alert by the weekend and you should all be under quarantine.

Please note: as with any interesting new disease, the symptoms evolve day by day. Please keep to this sequence all together, or the doctors may get confused.

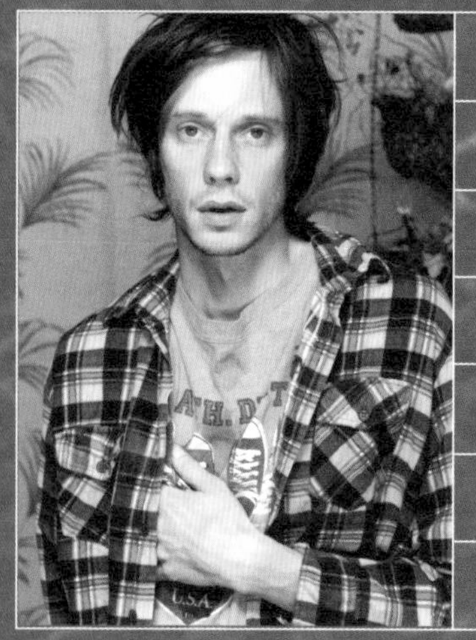

Day
Monday
Tuesday
Wednesday
Thursday
Friday
Saturday
Sunday

Symptoms	Experts you will meet
Your left eyeball is highly itchy, but at the back, so you can't scratch it.	Ophthalmologist
The itchiness has spread to your lower intestine, equally difficult to scratch.	Gastroenterologist
As well as the itching, you have developed an urge to urinate constantly.	Urologist
As you try to urinate, you hear music in your head, specifically Russian classical symphonic pieces.	ENT consultant
Your heart feels like it has synchronized to the beat of the Russian music, and that it will stop when the piece ends.	Cardiologist, psychiatrist
The itch has stopped, but your frontal lobe is feeling mushier than usual. The best way you can describe it is that your brain is melting. Get round to mentioning you just got back from trekking in Borneo last week.	Neurosurgeon, neurologist, immunologist, haematologist, parasitologist, epidemiologist
You have recovered overnight; perhaps it was a false alarm or a cold. You'd like to leave the camp and go home now please.	Lawyer

Monday 29

Tuesday 30

Wednesday 1

Thursday 2

Friday 3

Saturday 4

Sunday 5

Monday 6

Tuesday 7

Wednesday 8

Thursday 9

Friday 10

Saturday 11

Sunday 12

Benrik Charter Flight Week

Go on holiday together!

Two years ago, Benrik readers travelled together to invade the tiny village of Svankaer, Denmark. This task proved so popular that we are making it a regular feature. This week, you are to go on holiday with other congenial Diary readers, following the itinerary opposite.

The Aparthotel Fiesta Tropico is situated in a stunning location in the heart of Magaluf, not far from the beach and within walking distance of the resort's vibrant nightspots. It features a "freeform" swimming pool and a snack bar open late. During the day, enjoy the many organized leisure activities - or just laze by the pool! In the evening, visit the nearby BCM nightclub and dance until dawn. Book it through www.thomson.co.uk. Aparthotel Fiesta Tropico: Carrer Blanca 8, Magaluf 07182, Spain.

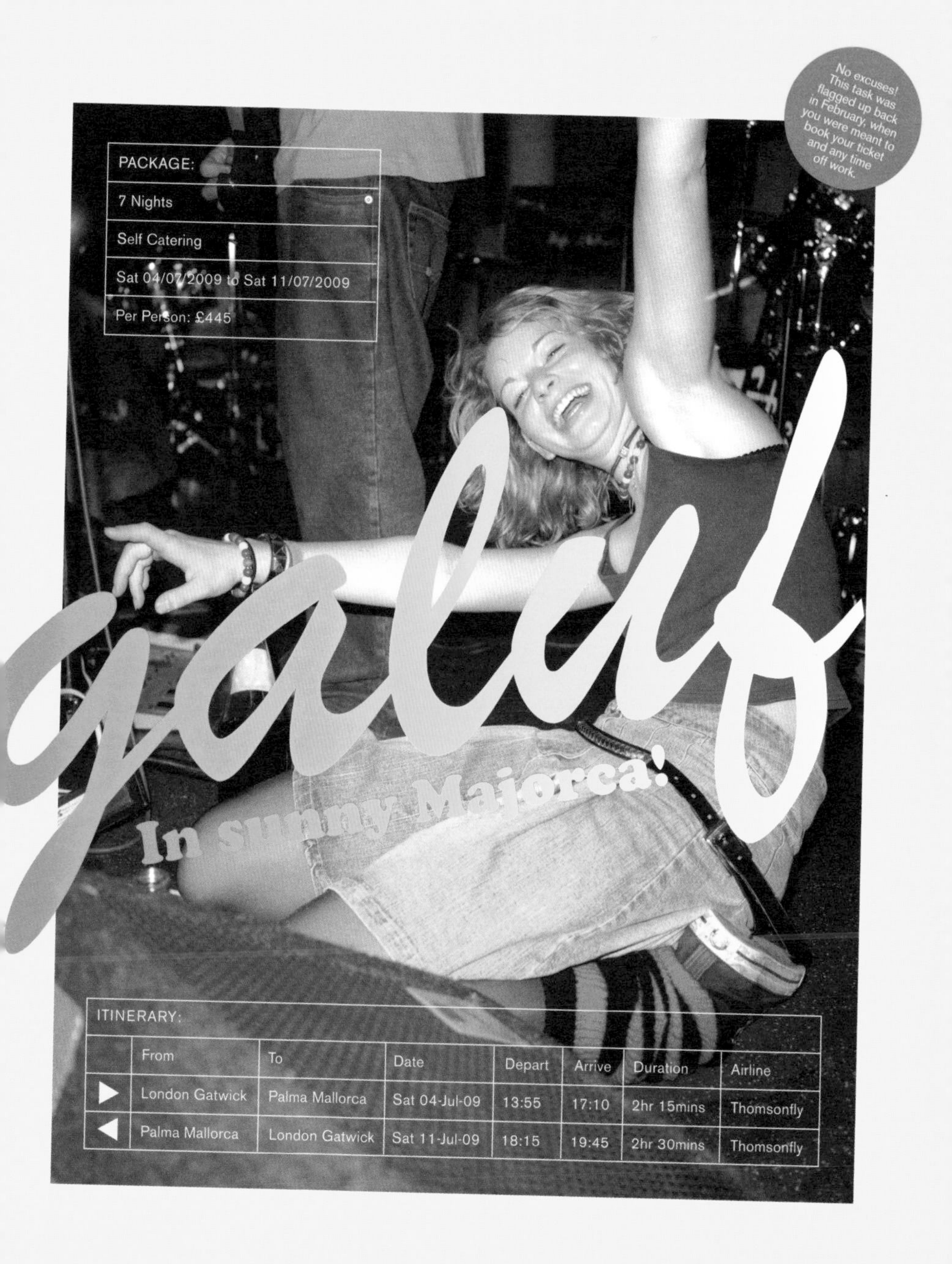

To discuss the week's plans and see who else is going,
go to www.benrik.co.uk and find the relevant message board.

INSIDER TRADING WEEK

1. Insider tip: "My uncle finds oil for BP and has just been sent off to the Black Sea urgently"
   Action: Buy BP shares
   Estimated gain: +80%

2. Insider tip: "I work for Cadbury's design agency - they're launching a new healthy chocolate creme egg in time for Easter"
   Action: Buy Cadbury shares
   Estimated gain: + 40%

3. Insider tip: "My girlfriend works for the local council. They're loosening up building regulations next month, it's a nationwide thing apparently"
   Action: Buy Barratt Homes
   Estimated gain: +25%

4. Insider tip: "My neighbour has just been caught by his wife with an underage rent boy. He's Chairman of Globocorp plc."
   Action: Sell Globocorp plc shares
   Estimated gain: +95%

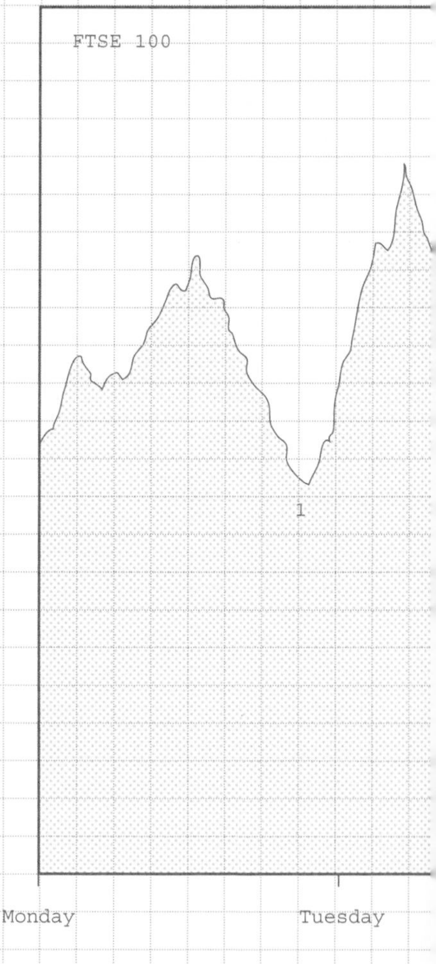

Benrik readers form a circle of trust, a community of like-minded people whose allegiance goes deeper than that of mere friends or family. It's time to profit from that trust. This week, everyone must report whatever confidential information they may glean from their company or government job, so that fellow Benrikians may gain by it.

Note: Don't hold back! The smallest details may be lucrative, as long as they're not already in the public domain.

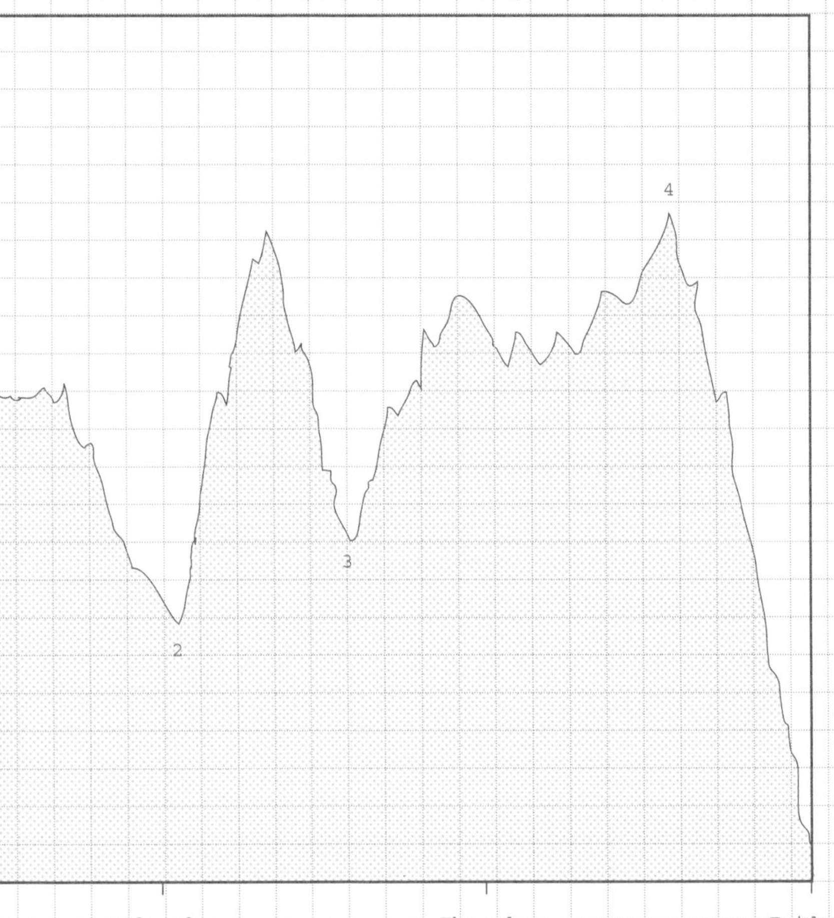

Monday 13

Tuesday 14

Wednesday 15

Thursday 16

Friday 17

Saturday 18

Sunday 19

Monday 20

Tuesday 21

Wednesday 22

Thursday 23

Friday 24

Saturday 25

Sunday 26

This week, uglify yourself to escape from the tyranny of appearance. Violate the canons of contemporary beauty one by one and see if it makes any difference to the way others treat you, or more importantly, how you feel about yourself.

MONDAY: GROW A SPOT
Rubbing your skin with wheat germ oil is meant to do the trick.

THURSDAY: GO WITHOUT SLEEP ALL NIGHT
They don't call it "beauty sleep" for nothing.

FRIDAY: START CHAIN-SMOKING
This will put the finishing touch to your new complexion.

TUESDAY: STOP BRUSHING YOUR TEETH
Toothpaste is an expensive con.

WEDNESDAY: STOP WASHING YOUR HAIR
Better still, shave it off.
In patches.

SATURDAY: AVOID SUNLIGHT
It makes you look like you've
been outside.

SUNDAY: STOP SMILING
Congratulations! Your beauty
now lies entirely within.

Already ugly? Rejoice! This week, you will be one of many.

SQUATTING WEEK

Squatting is normally associated with unwashed proto-anarchists, but it is in fact quite legal, provided you observe certain rules. This week, ditch your attachment to the shibboleth of private property: find an unoccupied building and move in. By the end of the week, you will have become more alive to this basic truth: we are all squatters on God's green earth. Squatting Guidelines:

Finding a suitable place to squat

There are dozens of thousands of empty properties in the UK alone. Don't go for the more heavily fenced-off ones, as their owners are probably more uptight. Instead, look for somewhere that's clearly been boarded up for a while but has become a bit run down; ideally, it will have been vandalised, so you can enter without actually breaking in - which is illegal.

Access to your squat

As with any property, the first thing you should do as a new occupier is change the locks, and secure access (i.e. repair the vandalised entrance). Once you have "exclusive access" to the property, you occupy it legally, and the owner cannot have you evicted without proper legal process. Obviously, this only goes for properties that are not lived in at the time; you cannot legitimately squat in someone's flat while they've popped off on holiday for a week, for example.

At home in your squat

Do not conform to the usual stereotypes of squatting by lighting dangerous brasiers, dealing drugs, or failing to observe basic hygiene. You might as well make your stay pleasant by decorating your squat with some knick-knacks and a couple of throws. A few geraniums on the window sill will do wonders for your relationship with the neighbours, and the image of squatting in general. Touch up a few walls in some contemporary pastel shades while you're at it, and by the end of the week the owner will thank you!

Legal niggles

Squatting is much misunderstood, and therefore may attract some unwelcome attention. Legally, as long as you are there, owners may not repossess the property without going to court. Do not open the door to police; speak to them through the letterbox. Should they decide to arrest you, remember you are entitled to call a lawyer. If all else fails, show them this book which will reassure them you mean well.

Monday 27

Tuesday 28

Wednesday 29

Thursday 30

Friday 31

Saturday 1

Sunday 2

Monday 3

Tuesday 4

Wednesday 5

Thursday 6

Friday 7

Saturday 8

Sunday 9

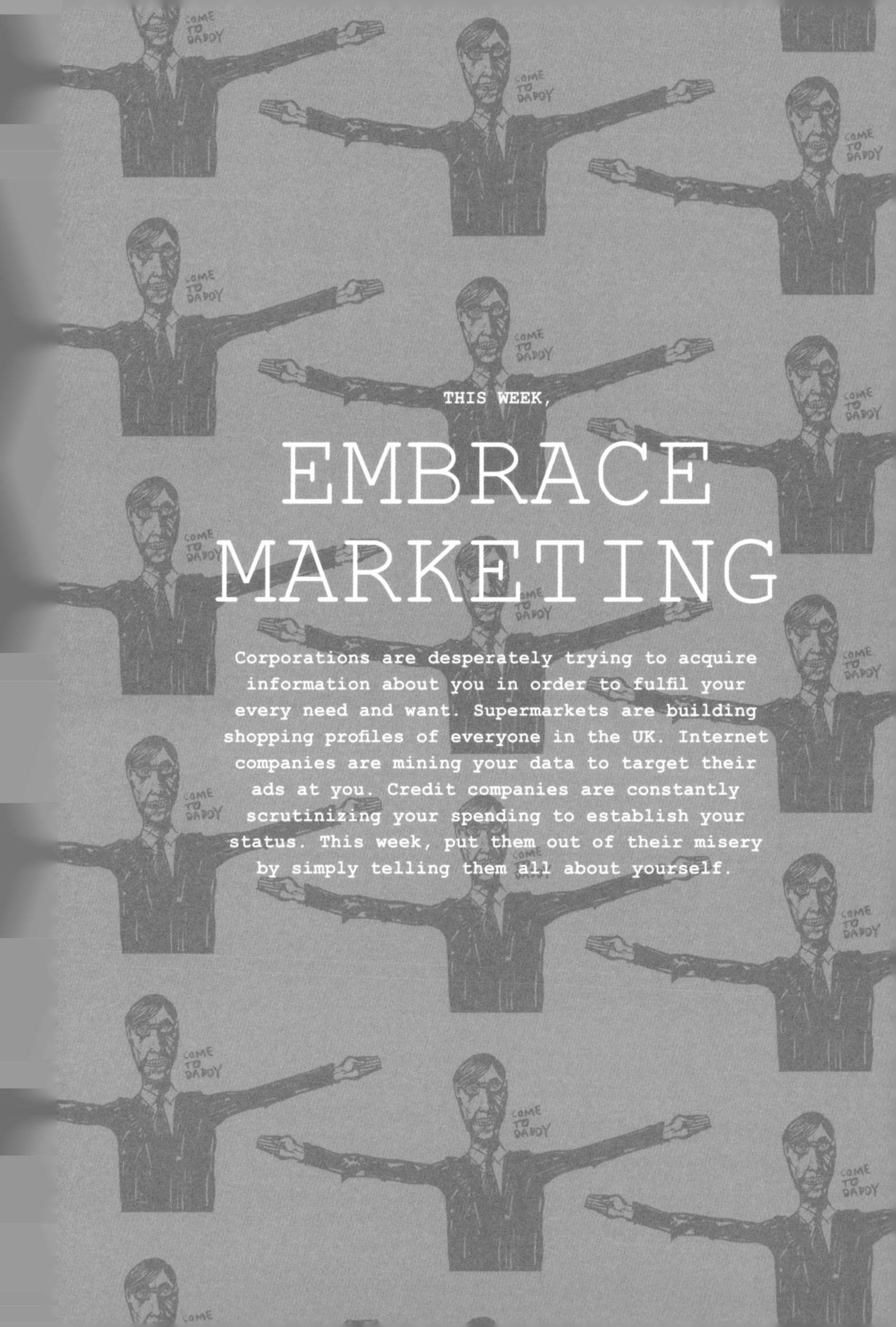

THIS WEEK,

EMBRACE MARKETING

Corporations are desperately trying to acquire information about you in order to fulfil your every need and want. Supermarkets are building shopping profiles of everyone in the UK. Internet companies are mining your data to target their ads at you. Credit companies are constantly scrutinizing your spending to establish your status. This week, put them out of their misery by simply telling them all about yourself.

Example:

Hi there

This is some information about me, that you may use for commercial marketing purposes to sell me products.

My name is Darren Rowe and I was born in Portsmouth in 1974. My father worked for the ferry company, my mother was a nurse – in terms of consumer segmentation, I would hazard we were a C1 or C2 family. I had a happy childhood, until my parents divorced when I was 10. My Dad remarried, to a B1. It was pretty miserable for me; her kids got all the toys – which is why I now can't control my spending, making me a good prospect for your special offers.

Anyway, I ran away from home a few times, and that messed up my education. I could have been a B1B2 but now I'm a C2 really if I'm honest. I've been working at a printer's for the last five years, on a salary of £23,000. It's not much but it gets me by, although I rely on the credit cards a lot (Natwest Visa, £4,541 balance, limit £6,500 as well as Nationwide, £2,980 balance, £3,000 limit).

I spend most of my disposable income on the following items: DVDs (12%), consumer electronics (24%), car (19% – a Ford Fiesta F-reg), food (26%), alcohol (15%). My favourite TV programmes are *Top Gear* and *Never Mind the Buzzcocks*. Unusually for my socio-economic demographic, I'm not that into football.

My home address is: 45 Dewksbury Road, Guildford HW3 4RF. My email address is d.rowe871@blueyonder.co.uk.

I look forward to hearing from you!

Demand your data: Under the Data Protection Act 1998, UK citizens have the right to request details of the data held about them and are entitled to correct it. To help you in this week's task, write to every organization who might hold data on you and find out what they know. This includes: supermarkets, government departments, websites, schools, hospitals. Don't write to Benrik though, we've sold it on a long time ago.

THURSDAY

Stay at home. By now, the regulars will have become accustomed to you and will enjoy speculating on the reasons for your absence, which as everyone knows makes the heart grow fonder.

FRIDAY

Account for last night's absence with a story the regulars will empathize with – the bailiffs came round unexpectedly, or your dog got run over. If the story is good enough, they will buy you a drink, a sure sign of acceptance.

SATURDAY

The pinnacle of the week: buy everyone a round, flirt with bar staff of the opposite sex, and engage in banter with the other regulars. Get drunk and be the last to leave. Vomiting outside is optional, but constitutes a traditional way of marking your territory.

SUNDAY

By now, you should be firmly established as a regular. If the others try to dissuade strangers from sitting in your seat, you know you have arrived. Ditch your old friends and bask in the warm beery embrace of your new social circle.

Notes: If you are already a regular at your local, obviously select a different one. Also, if on Day 1 you spot other likely Benrik readers sitting in a corner, pick another pub, as the regulars may be overwhelmed by the influx of newcomers.

"Cheers!" Week

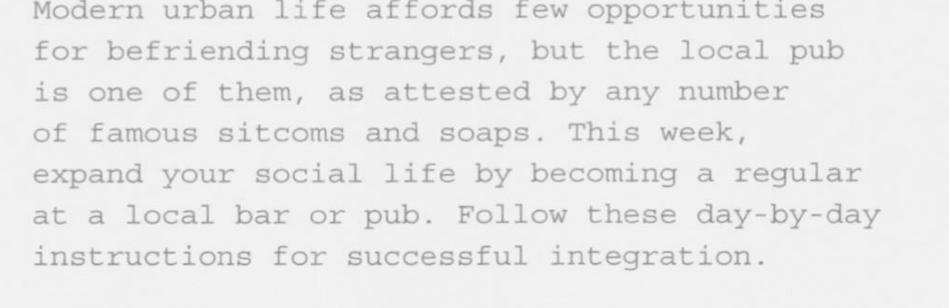

Modern urban life affords few opportunities for befriending strangers, but the local pub is one of them, as attested by any number of famous sitcoms and soaps. This week, expand your social life by becoming a regular at a local bar or pub. Follow these day-by-day instructions for successful integration.

MONDAY
Pick a corner and sit there all evening: that way you won't crowd the regulars, but they will notice you. Wear a memorable item of clothing, which will become the basis for your identity, as in "Where's Bowtie tonight?"

TUESDAY
Tonight you may sit at the bar, but do not initiate interaction. Order an unusual drink, like a banana daiquiri, which will provide a conversational opener for the regulars e.g. "You like banana daiquiris, then, do you?"

WEDNESDAY
This evening, you should nod to others as you take your position at the bar, and talk to the barman as you order your regular drink. You will have monitored the regulars' conversation and should bring up suitable topics of interest, which they may latch on to.

Monday 10

Tuesday 11

Wednesday 12

Thursday 13

Friday 14

Saturday 15

Sunday 16

Monday 17

Tuesday 18

Wednesday 19

Thursday 20

Friday 21

Saturday 22

Sunday 23

"Mañana mañana" Week

This week, do your bit to slow our society down. Our civilization is far too efficiency-minded. There are few tasks so important that they can't wait a few days for completion. Learning to relax and take your time will improve your life immeasurably - and probably delay your death. Others too will be grateful for the softer pace you impose.

Walk slowly
across pedestrian
crossings

Roll your tongue in
your mouth seven times
before speaking

Postpone all your
appointments to
next week

Drive at half
the speed limit

Don't get your card
out until you get
to the cash point

Object to
planning
applications

Gossip with the
checkout girl

LIFELONG
EDUCATION
WEEK
SUN

This week, call your ex-teachers and fill in any gaps in your education

Teachers are for life. Even if technically speaking you've left school, you can still call them with questions about lessons you missed or didn't fully understand at the time. If anything, they will be flattered by your continued interest in their subject, and the fact that you remember them at all.

Sample questions:

History:	"Who won the battle of Salamis?"
Maths:	"If xy = 9, what is the square root of z?"
Geography:	"What is the average pressure in an anticyclone?"
English	"'To be or not to be'. Which is it?"
French	"What is the plural of Monsieur?"
Chemistry	"What type of element usually forms acidic oxides?"

Teacher crushes: at 15, you couldn't do much about your clumsy sexual crush on a teacher. Ten to twenty years later, it's a different story. Let them know how you felt about them and find out if they still think of you as a potential star pupil.

Monday 24

Tuesday 25

Wednesday 26

Thursday 27

Friday 28

Saturday 29

Sunday 30

Monday 31

Tuesday 1

Wednesday 2

Thursday 3

Friday 4

Saturday 5

Sunday 6

THIS WEEK: HIRE A PROSTITUTE FOR A NON-SEXUAL PURPOSE
Prostitutes see a different side of life. This week, hire one for a couple of hours and ask her to fill you in on the sleazier aspects of the human condition. Prostitutes are tired of the constant sex, and will welcome the opportunity for more varied activity. Good activities to enjoy with your prostitute:

VISIT THE BRITISH MUSEUM

Prostitution is the oldest job in the world, so many of the artefacts here will relate to it.

SEE A CHICK FLICK

Prostitutes see men as they really are, and will be able to shed light on the plot's verisimilitude.

GO TO THE GYM TOGETHER

Staying in shape is a must; your prostitute should be able to double as a personal trainer.

PLAY CHESS

Just so you can tell your grandchildren that you were once beaten at chess by a prostitute grandmaster.

SHOP FOR LINGERIE

The prostitute will advise you as to the latest fashions for your wife/girlfriend.

WATCH THE SUNSET

Prostitutes don't get asked to do this much, and it should prompt a bout of revealing introspection.

Rates: The going rate for two hours might average £200, depending on the class of prostitute. If you can't afford £200, try negotiating a shorter time, like £10 for a quick chat over a cup of tea. Female readers may hire a gigolo this week if they prefer. However: remember that the purpose of this week is to understand the sleazier side of humanity, which female prostitutes obviously see a lot more of.

The individuals depicted here are models, and not prostitutes or their clients. They have been chosen to make the point that prostitutes look entirely homely when not on the job.

Important

Send Attach Address Fonts Colors

From: Squigley@googlemail.com

To: FredHarris89@gmail.com, Marilou_follain@yahoo.com, r.bodson@gtbiz.co.uk, markjb13@blueyonder.co.uk, katherine.blyth45@myspace.com, biff@telesports.nl, info@brickcabs.com, moshi.kobayashi@qualiacomm.jp, kieran66@yopla.fr, emma.spencer@dti.gov.uk, mikebardon@bardon.co.uk, tigger977@telia.de, alexei@spotnik.ru, bridgenie4000@telewest.com, hornyrabbit@smfriendfinder.com, bill@marsdenfamily.com, jonnyxxx@blueyonder.com, djsam@electronica.co.nz, admin@fgpsupplies.co.uk, christopher.dehet87@wachovia.com, pesesr.glenn@usfa.af.mil, chrsteen_rmns@yahoo.com, chrysanthi_skyyx@yahoo.com, chubbsboyf@yahoo.co.uk, chuckskitsche447@aol.com, blackknight@hotmail.co.uk, pcharming@sbcglobal.net, mindy_lontern@boltblue.co.uk, circus_pony96@hotmail.com, citygent155@msn.com, ucl3119@bristol.ac.uk, timb@netstar.co.za, giogler@yahoo.com, hamster144@cox.net, giovanni_van_stronkster@hotmail.com, zorgelement666@verizon.net, krikku@hotmail.co.uk, gimp_87@hotmail.com, itubre@hotmail.com, Glamourdawg88@blueyonder.co.uk, Thelma196@comcast.net, Jliz_81@hotmail.com, dyingfaintly@homail.com, loser12069@hotmail.com trivade45@yahoo.com, lotoflaughs@soon.com, sales2@readings.com.au, luisloper_89@mac.com, billioschultz@optsnet.com.au, rov8u@hotmail.com, ppaddict7@aol.co.uk, wperold@rollcom.co.fr, 989Thief@aol.com, luann3@luanna.com, tomberthellet@hotmail.com, dogmeister6@spray.se, minimargarta@aol.com tinksey139@hotmai.com, pumpkinator_56@ wmconnect.com, nogo_vitamins@hotmail.com, punky-emokid4789@hotmail.com, zilverii@ rugers.edu, simone_horris@virginmedia.co.uk, btjones@rush.uscg.mil, frankjree_uk@hotmail.com, sk8trgrl22687@aol.com

Subject: Important

Dear friend,
You don't know me, but I thought you should know this: sprinkling plain old gruyère over your risottos tastes delicious and makes them much less gooey than parmesan does, for half the price. I discovered this myself serendipitously last night (I had run out of parmesan). I have nothing to gain financially from telling you this, and I am sorry if it's not relevant to your eating habits. Still, I hope you find the information useful. Sorry for the "spam"!
Best
Sarah Quigley
Bicester, UK

Positive Spamming Week

Spamming only has a bad name because the individuals who engage in it are usually pornographers and rip-off merchants. There is nothing intrinsically wrong with unsolicited communication, however, as long as it enhances the life of the people who receive it. This week, engage in positive spamming: send useful unsolicited emails to dozens of lucky recipients.

1. GATHER ADDRESSES
Professional spammers use "spambots" to harvest email addresses from the web. You are a beginner though, so find them manually by browsing through blogs, MySpace profiles etc.

2. PICK A SUBJECT
Think of an interesting subject with broad appeal. Examples: novel solutions to global warming, life-saving tips, little-known sexual proclivities of world leaders. Steer clear of defamatory statements though.

3. COMPOSE YOUR EMAIL
Apologize upfront for the unsolicited nature of your email, but point out you are trying to redeem spam by making it more useful. Invite feedback on whether the recipient considers you have achieved your goal, and provide an "unsubscribe" option.

4. SEND
Do not send bulk email all in one go, as your ISP will notice and blacklist you. Send the spam in batches of fifty at a time. Should your ISP complain or threaten to ban you, reiterate the argument above, and refer them to this book.

Monday 7

Tuesday 8

Wednesday 9

Thursday 10

Friday 11

Saturday 12

Sunday 13

Monday 14

Tuesday 15

Wednesday 16

Thursday 17

Friday 18

Saturday 19

Sunday 20

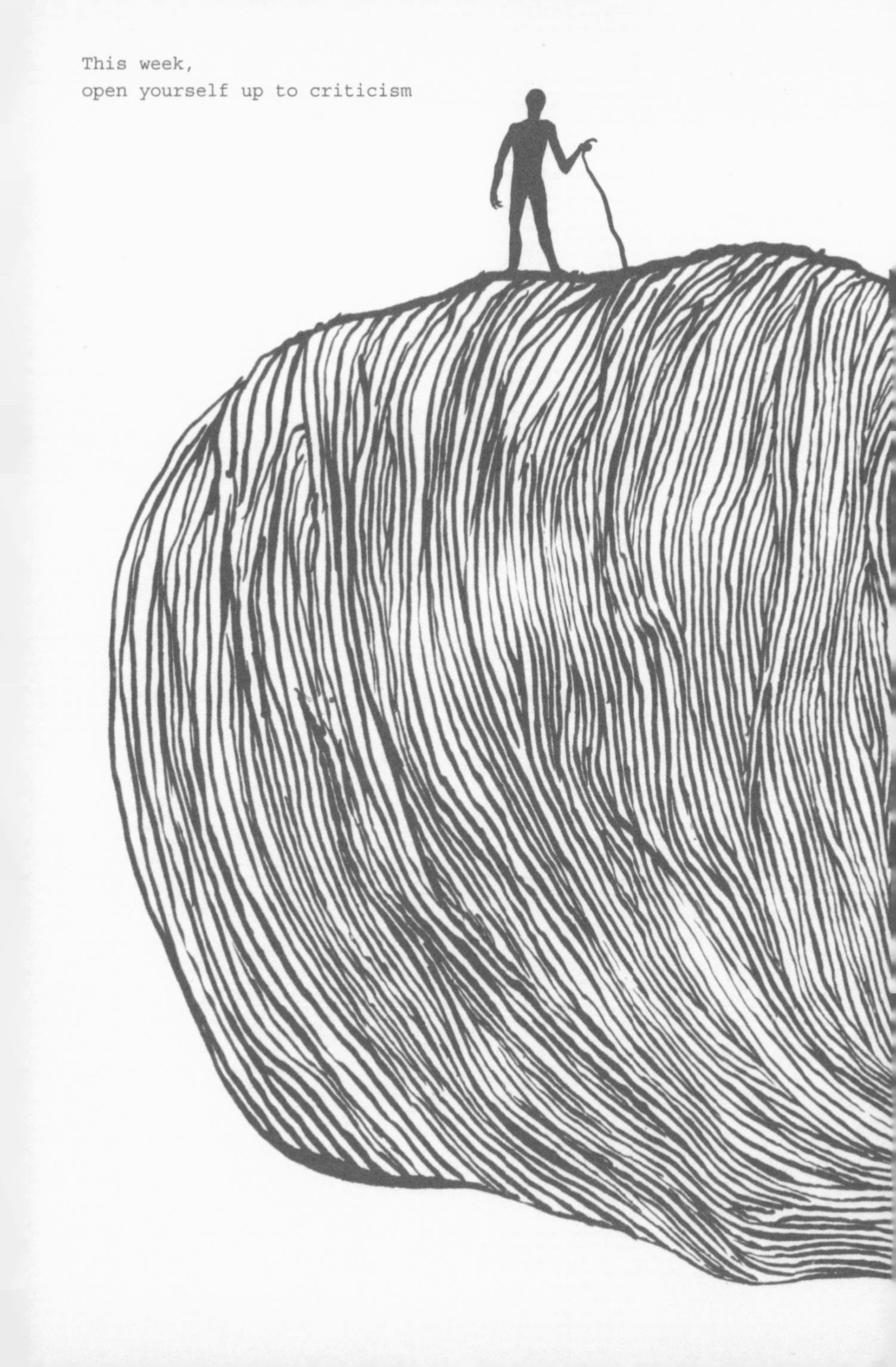
This week,
open yourself up to criticism

The path to true self-knowledge is fraught and tortuous. Often, we may only attain it through the glare of others. This week, take the single thing you have ever created that you are most proud of, and ask for an undiluted critique. The work could be anything, from that draft novel you've hidden in your bottom drawer, to photos of the wedding you planned so carefully; from your PhD thesis to your childhood doodles - anything that touches a nerve and reveals your soul.

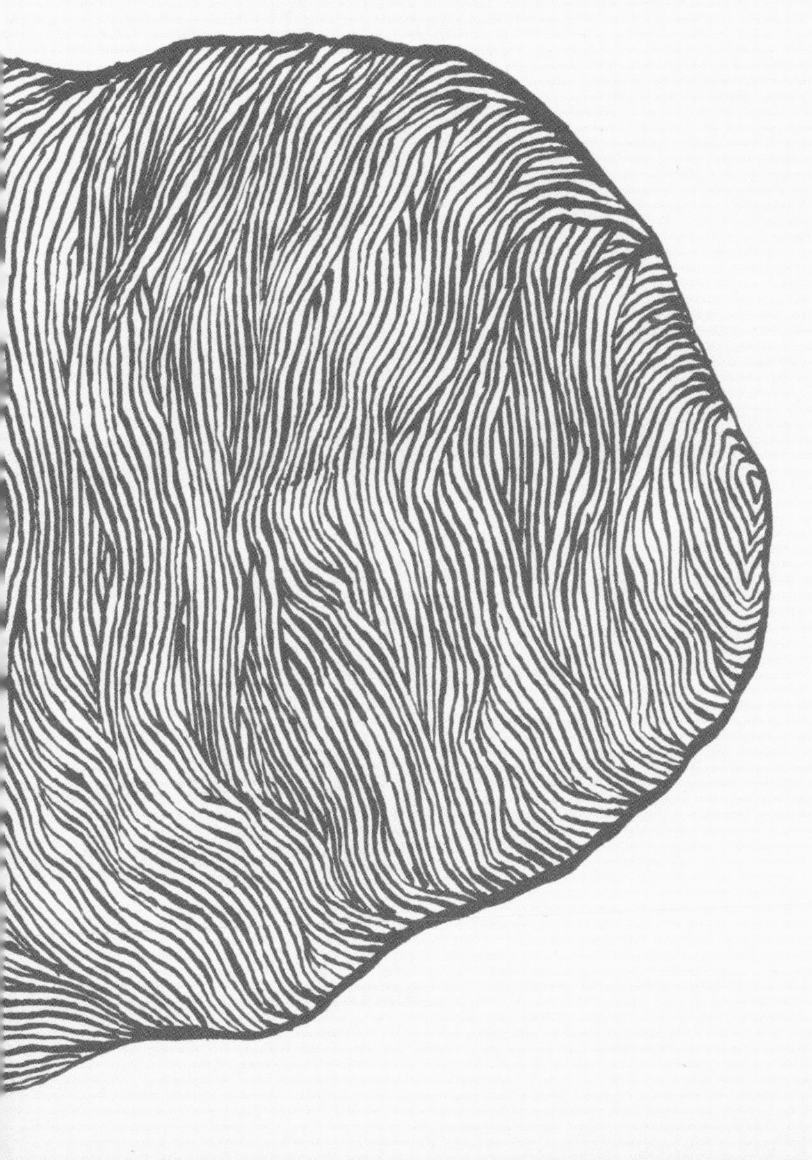

Post it on www.thiswebsitewillchangeyourlife.com and await the feedback.

COMMUNISM WEEK

Communism failed largely because it was implemented in an unnecessarily insensitive manner. A more gradual approach might have won more converts. This week, Benrik are giving communism one more go, but on a manageable scale. All readers are to pool their week's earnings, and Benrik will redistribute them equally. If everyone is happy with the result, we will extend the experiment, first to the rest of the month, then to the year, then to the world.

Full Name:

Address:

Occupation:

Country:

Currency:

Earnings for the week of Sept 21 to Sept 27 (inclusive):

To calculate your week's earnings, multiply your monthly net earnings by 0.233 (7/30).

I hereby contribute my weekly earnings to my Benrik comrades, on the understanding that they will be redistributed on an equal basis between contributors. If I have earned more than the average, I will therefore lose out financially. If I have earned less, I will gain. I accept that this is all for the greater good of the Benrik collective, the community spirit of readers, and that it constitutes perhaps the last chance for communism to redeem itself in the eyes of the public.

Signed:

Dated: / /

Please send cheques to Benrik Limited, c/o Macmillan, 20 New Wharf Road, London N1 9RR, UK, along with proof of earnings (a PAYE slip for employees, invoices for the self-employed countersigned by a qualified accountant, bank statements with dividend and other earnings for company directors, benefit slips for the unemployed, grant documentation for students). Include an SAE for the return communist earnings cheque. Benrik will divide the total cleared sum (after bank charges) and return cheques in sterling. Calculations will be posted on www.thiswebsitewillchangeyourlife.com by October 5 when cheques have cleared.

Monday 21

Tuesday 22

Wednesday 23

Thursday 24

Friday 25

Saturday 26

Sunday 27

Monday 28

Tuesday 29

Wednesday 30

Thursday 1

Friday 2

Saturday 3

Sunday 4

Local Pub

This drinking establishment is affiliated with [Your name], who gets upset if you fail to respect its staff. Thank you.

Local Supermarket

This retail outlet is friends with [Your name]. And [Your name] very much frowns on anyone who shoplifts from their friends.

Local Restaurant

This restaurant is patronised by [Your name].
It would be a great shame for you and your family if you didn't patronise it also.

Local newsagent

[Your name]
loves this newsagent as if he were their own flesh and blood. Disrespecting him would be like disrespecting them – not a good idea.

Godfather Week

This week, offer your protection to local businesses, reassuring them that they are under your wing. There need be no formal agreement in place; just tell them quietly that, should they run into any kind of unforeseen trouble, they can call you to help fix it. Emphasize that there is no obligation on their part - however, at some point in the future, they may be able or indeed called upon to return the favour. Fill these signs in and leave them for the owners to post in their shop windows.

THIS WEEK,
SYNCHRONIZE
SOCIETY'S
WATCHES

It is no surprise that society is fractured when we don't all run on the same exact time. Help us all achieve military levels of coordination this week: ask everyone the time and reset their watch to the exact second if they have it wrong.

In the UK, the body responsible for keeping the exact time is the National Physical Laboratory. Check with them that you have the right time before asking others to change it. Call their helpline on +44 20 8943 6880, email enquiry@npl.co.uk, or write to: NPL, Hampton Road, Teddington, Middlesex, TW11 0LW, United Kingdom. Do not call the speaking clock, which is atomically imprecise.

& pastr

Monday 5

Tuesday 6

Wednesday 7

Thursday 8

Friday 9

Saturday 10

Sunday 11

Monday 12

Tuesday 13

Wednesday 14

Thursday 15

Friday 16

Saturday 17

Sunday 18

This week:
LIVE BEYOND YOUR MEANS

Capitalism's most destructive feature is not that it unleashes an unbridled consumerist frenzy, but that it regulates it, frustrating our desires and turning us into penny-pinching accountants, too scared to give rein to our appetite for life. This week, ignore protestant prudence and spend to excess. Fund your spending through any means you like: overdraft, bank loan, credit card, pawnbroker. It'll take the authorities at least a week to work out you can't afford it. Here is a useful phone number for when they do:

Consumer Credit Counselling Service
0800 138 1111

AND REMEMBER: IT'S ONLY MONEY.

It doesn't matter what you spend the money on as long as you can't afford it. Tailor your extravagance to your personal circumstances, for example:
Tramp: the most expensive booze your local off-licence can supply: £28.99
Student: a supply of top-class cocaine for those essay crises: £100
Burger flipper: dinner at The Ivy: £240
Public sector employee: designer label outfit, including shoes: £1,800
Private sector employee: Mercedes X-series: £150,000
City trader: minor Caribbean Island: £15,000,000

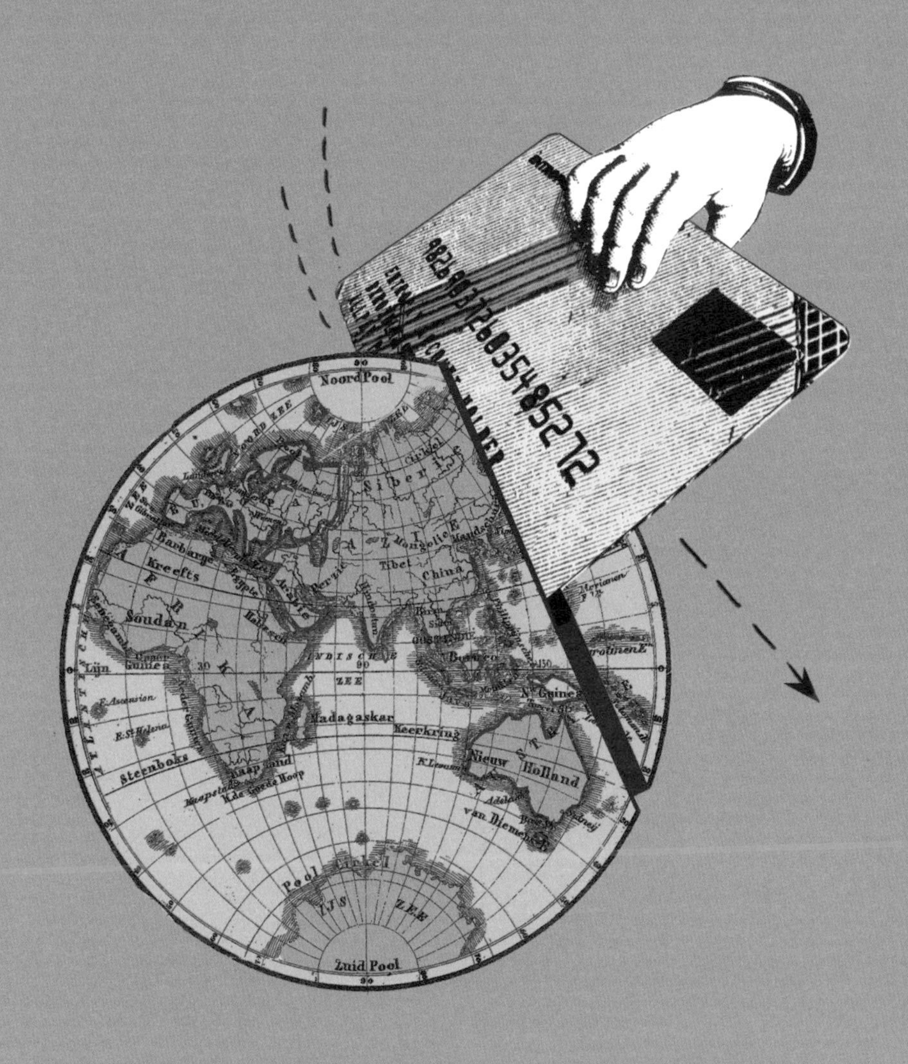

"Anyone who lives within their means
suffers from a lack of imagination"
Oscar Wilde

Feet have not done well out of civilization. Until the last few millennia, they were out in the open air. Now we enclose them in the dark for most of the day, perhaps, as French writer Georges Bataille claimed, because they remind us of our primeval struggle to leave the mud. This week, restore them to their former glory: take a beautiful photo of your best foot and post it on various foot-fetish websites to see if it excites admiration. Ask for feedback, respond to queries, indulge harmless fantasies - by the end of the week, your foot might well be the most famous part of you.

Start here: http://www.footfetishpartners.com

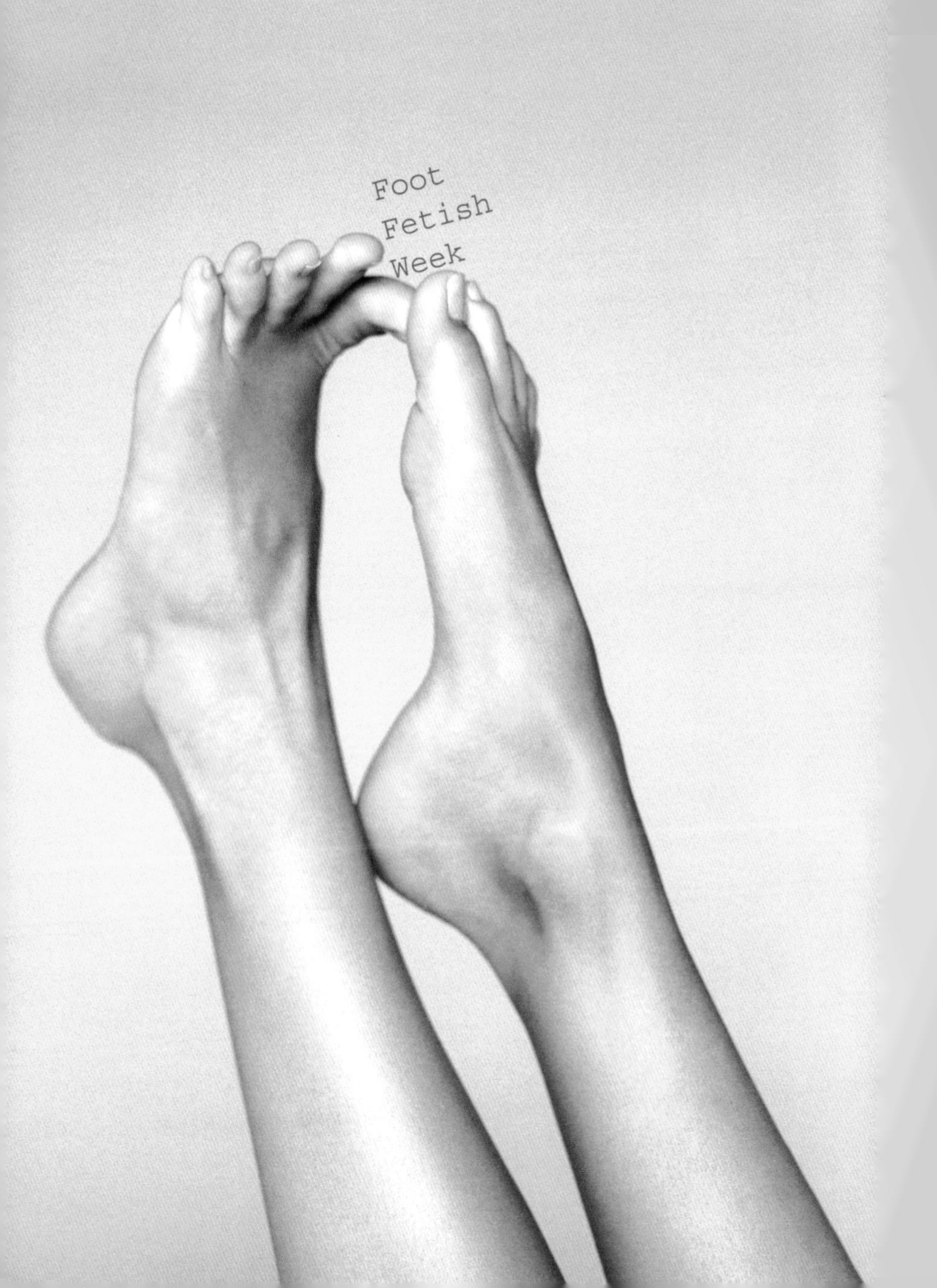
Foot
Fetish
Week

Monday 19

Tuesday 20

Wednesday 21

Thursday 22

Friday 23

Saturday 24

Sunday 25

Monday 26

Tuesday 27

Wednesday 28

Thursday 29

Friday 30

Saturday 31

Sunday 1

Benrik Babysitting Week

The dinosaurs are still around, they're just hiding

Santa Claus is a secular Satan

Sometimes 1+1=3

Benrik is your good uncle, the other one is a cyborg

Teachers are paid to lie to you

Tea is for girls, coffee is for boys

THIS WEEK, REPROGRAMME A CHILD WITH BENRIK VIEWS. Babysitting isn't just a boring way of earning not much money; it's an opportunity to contribute to a child's education. Either babysit a child of your acquaintance, or put a notice in a local shop advertising your services (£8/hour is the going rate). Wait until the parents have left, and instead of letting the child waste its time watching TV, read to him or her from the views below.

MAKE A SUGGESTION TO A
BILLIONAIRE THIS WEEK

Today's billionaires are cash-rich but imagination-starved. They are wealthy beyond past emperors' wildest dreams. And yet they do nothing of lasting vision with their money - our culture favours managerial types, more suited to acquiring fortunes penny by penny than spending it in suitably extravagant fashion. This week, come up with projects on a pharaonic scale, and email them to the super-rich. Remind them: you can't take it with you!

Your marble statue in space: immortality guaranteed. Estimated cost: $1 million to build + $120 million to blast into orbit.

Personal TV channel: commission the programmes you want to see. Estimated cost: $500 million a year.

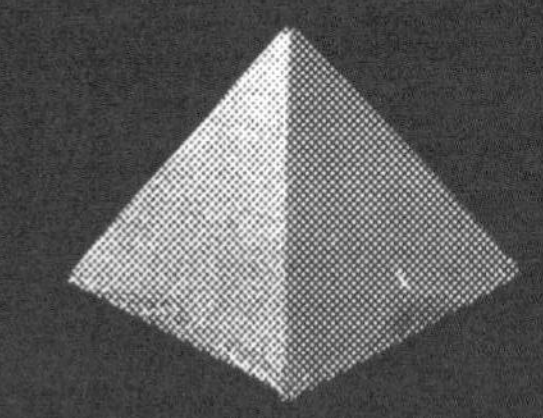

Hi-tech pyramid: enter history by the front door. Estimated cost: $1bn to buy one from Egyptian state + $1bn to refurbish.

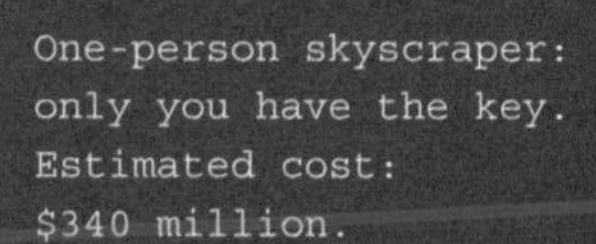

One-person skyscraper: only you have the key. Estimated cost: $340 million.

Hollywood star contracted to read bedtime story to your children. Estimated cost: $100,000 a night.

A 747 to write your name in vapour trails. Estimated cost: $200 million to buy, then $4,000,000/hour to fly.

For a list of UK billionaires, visit: www.sundaytimes.co.uk/richlist. Russian billionaires are a good bet, as they have a more open-minded outlook on how to spend their money, and are less shy than their British counterparts. On the downside, they are more open-minded about killing you if your idea displeases them. Overall, be sure to mention your suggestions are free and you don't want any money for them.

Monday 2

Tuesday 3

Wednesday 4

Thursday 5

Friday 6

Saturday 7

Sunday 8

Monday 9

Tuesday 10

Wednesday 11

Thursday 12

Friday 13

Saturday 14

Sunday 15

Week 46

1. FIND A PLOT
Ideally, you should look for slightly moist light clay soil. If you hit rocks, find another plot for your grave. Don't forget to ask the plot owner's permission.

2. PROCURE A SUITABLE SPADE
Go for quality: a solid forged blade with a round point shovel, an epoxy coated head and a hardwood shaft. This is no time for second best.

THIS WEEK, DIG YOUR OWN GRAVE: Digging one's own grave has negative connotations; it is usually associated with imminent death at the hands of sadistic paramilitary units. However there is no denying it does focus the mind on the meaning and value of life, and could thus be considered therapeutical. This week, your task is to find out: [illegible]llow the instructions above

3. MEASURE YOUR GRAVE
Leave 30cm around your body's footprint to allow room for your coffin. The usual depth is 6 foot, out of convention rather than scientific need.
4. DIG YOUR GRAVE
Digging is hard work. Wear proper boots. Keep your back as straight as possible and step on the spade to cut deeply into the soil.
5. LIE IN YOUR GRAVE
Reflect on your life and decide what to do with the rest of it (take a notepad). Don't fall asleep. Wear washable clothing. And mind the worms.
6. RESERVE YOUR GRAVE (OPTIONAL)
If you are pleased with your handiwork, see if you can reserve the plot for the day when you actually need it. If you don't wish to reserve it, make sure to fill it back in.*

Non-verbal communication week

Psychologists tell us that 85% of communication is non-verbal. This week dispense with the verbal 15% and concentrate on what's important. Only speak if strictly necessary, claiming to have a painful sore throat if need be; try to lead your normal life through physical cues alone. Paradoxically, your communication may be enriched as a result.

Write the things that you find you
cannot communicate without words here:

"Help, police!"

"I'd like to remortgage on the 7.9% rate APR"

Write the things you find you
can communicate non-verbally here:

"Nice weather we're having"

"I fancy you"

"I want a divorce"

Monday 16

Tuesday 17

Wednesday 18

Thursday 19

Friday 20

Saturday 21

Sunday 22

Monday 23

Tuesday 24

Wednesday 25

Thursday 26

Friday 27

Saturday 28

Sunday 29

Animals are easy to love - they are close to us in the evolutionary tree. Insects, however, evoke a preconscious feeling of revulsion. Test the limits and the nature of your capacity for affection this week, by learning to love an individual insect.

Monday
CATCH YOUR INSECT:
Get off to a good start by bein
gentle.

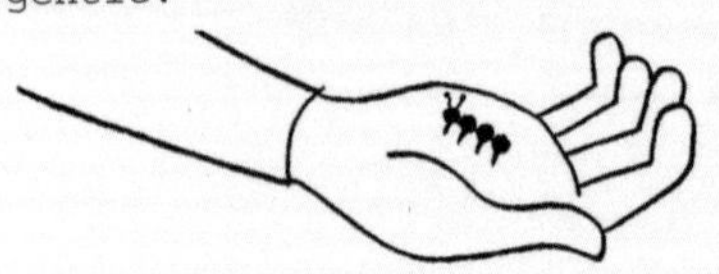

Fly....................
Spider.................
Ant....................
Caterpillar............
Not sure what the hell it is...

This week, make friends

Thursday
HANG OUT WITH YOUR INSECT:
Learn what's unique about their insect personality.

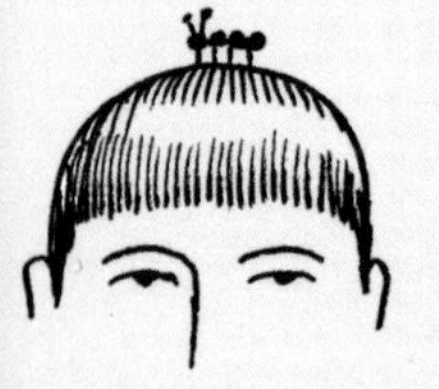

Inquisitive... ☐
Outgoing...... ☐
Introvert..... ☐
Sociable...... ☐
Thoughtful.... ☐

Friday
LOVE YOUR INSECT:
By now you know each other, so have a nice cuddle.

You
Enjoyed the cuddle....... ☐
Didn't enjoy the cuddle.. ☐

Insect
Enjoyed the cuddle....... ☐
Didn't enjoy the cuddle.. ☐

Tuesday

NAME YOUR INSECT:

This will help anthropomorphize it.

Derek.......................... ☐
John........................... ☐
Lucy........................... ☐
Michael........................ ☐
Steven......................... ☐
Cecilia........................ ☐
Rowan.......................... ☐
Eva............................ ☐
Other:......................... ☐

Wednesday

FEED YOUR INSECT:

True friends share their food.

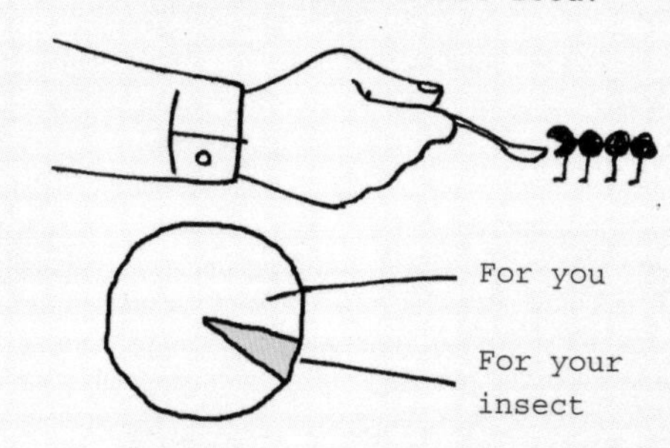

with an insect

Saturday

KILL YOUR INSECT:

If you can't, then you have grown attached to it, bravo.

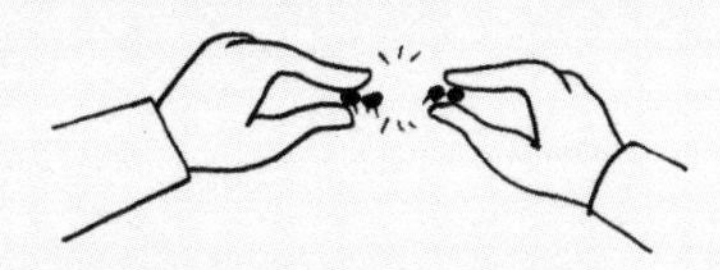

I couldn't bring myself to kill it................ ☐
I stamped on it........... ☐
I swatted it.............. ☐
I sprayed it.............. ☐

Sunday

NOW APPLY WHAT YOU HAVE LEARNT TO HUMAN BEINGS.

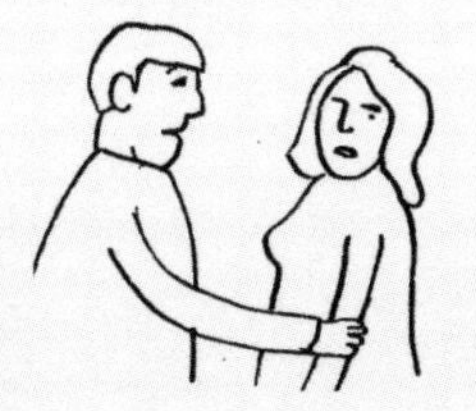

You may look disgusting but I love you darling!

This week, let Benrik track your location via your mobile phone

Benrik are very enthusiastic about mobile phone GPS-tracking technology, as it will enable them to maintain a higher degree of control over their followers, ensuring that no opportunity for life-change is missed. They are betting that by now (December 2009, 18 months after the book goes to print), this technology will be mainstream and fully-integrated with Google maps or some other such service (visit thiswebsitewillchangeyourlife.com to see which particular application has been deemed most suitable and to give Benrik your number).

Accordingly, this week you are to allow Benrik to track your location, and give you tasks to follow in real time.

Benrik reader # 290,112:

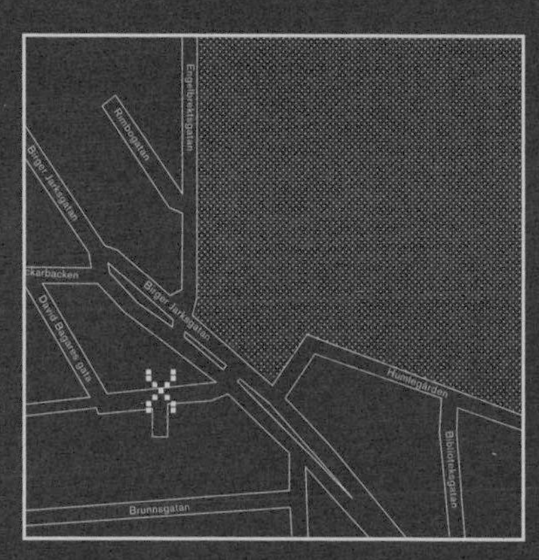

Turn left into the park, where you are to spend the afternoon acting as park scarecrow.

Benrik reader # 5,675:

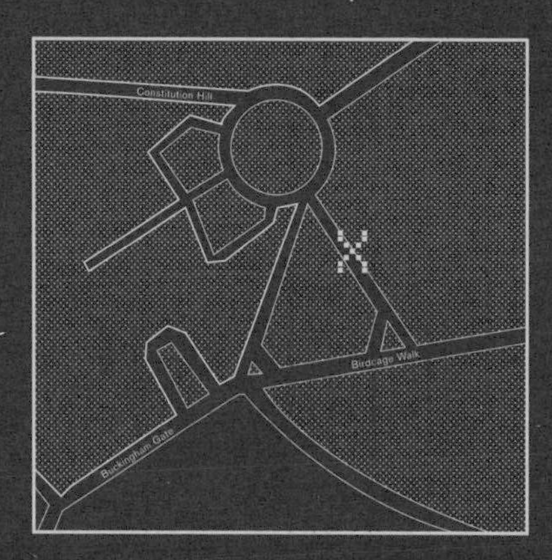

Ask a Buckingham Palace guard to autograph your copy of the Diary.

Benrik reader # 78,801:

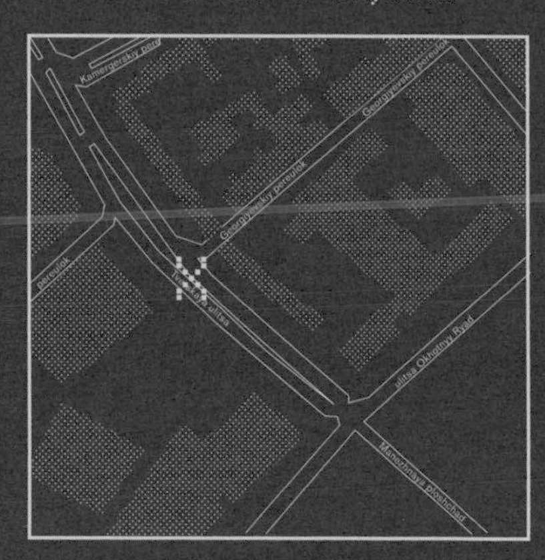

Stay put until further orders from Benrik.

Benrik reader # 34,587:

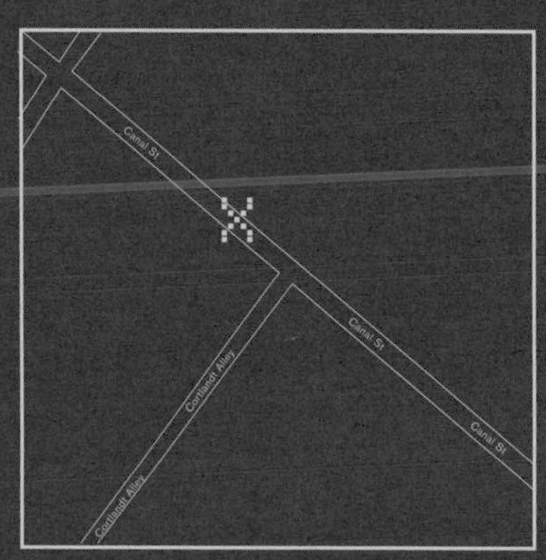

Meet Benrik reader # 102,770 at the counter of Starbucks on Canal St and hug each other like brothers.

Monday 30

Tuesday 1

Wednesday 2

Thursday 3

Friday 4

Saturday 5

Sunday 6

Monday 7

Tuesday 8

Wednesday 9

Thursday 10

Friday 11

Saturday 12

Sunday 13

Closure Week

Everyone must go through their share of failed relationships before they find "the one". This week, call up all your ex-partners, arrange to catch up over a coffee or dinner, and analyze why the relationship failed. This will ensure you get rid of your unresolved emotional baggage and become a much sunnier person by the end of the week – ready to love anew. Use the form opposite.

CLOSURE FORM

Ex's name:..

Details of relationship:...

....

....

Ex-boyfriend ☐
Ex-girlfriend ☐
Ex-husband ☐
Ex-wife ☐

CURRENT STATUS ☐
Married with kids.. ☐
In a long-term relationship......................... ☐
Engaging in meaningless flings.................... ☐
Hasn't met anyone since you........................ ☐
Has changed sexual orientation since you ☐

THE SEX WAS:
Hot! ☐
Hot to begin with ☐
Cold ☐
Non-existent ☐
Scary ☐

LENGTH OF RELATIONSHIP:
................years ....months ....days
Dates of relationship:
.... / .... / .... to .... / .... / ....

DETAILS OF CLOSURE
Whose fault was it the relationship failed?
Yours ☐ Theirs ☐ Disputed ☐
Official reason the relationship failed:...
Your apology for something you'd done:...
Their apology for something they'd done:...
Unwanted advice provided by you:..
Unwanted advice provided by them:...
Abuse to vent out your frustrations:...
Abuse to vent out their frustrations:..
Offer of one-night stand for old times' sake:
Accepted ☐ Declined ☐

Photocopy this form for each of your ex-partners. Be sure to show them to your current partner, so they understand you better.

THIS WEEK, SAVE THE PLANET AT ANY COST

The Earth is in terminal danger, so let us all drop the usual social niceties. This week, do whatever it takes to cut mankind's consumption of natural resources and help bring our precious ecosystem back into balance.

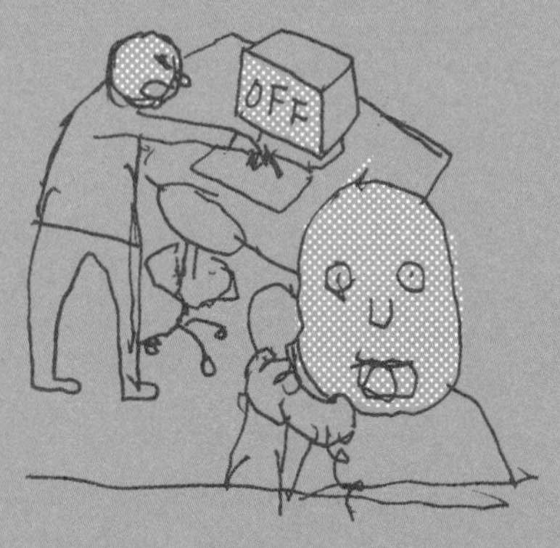

MONDAY

Turn other people's electrical appliances off while they're not looking

TUESDAY

Turn off the water in pu
toilets while people's h
are still soapy

THURSDAY

Discreetly knock light bulbs in other people's homes to break the filament

FRIDAY

Monitor the office toilet and discourage people from unnecessary flushing

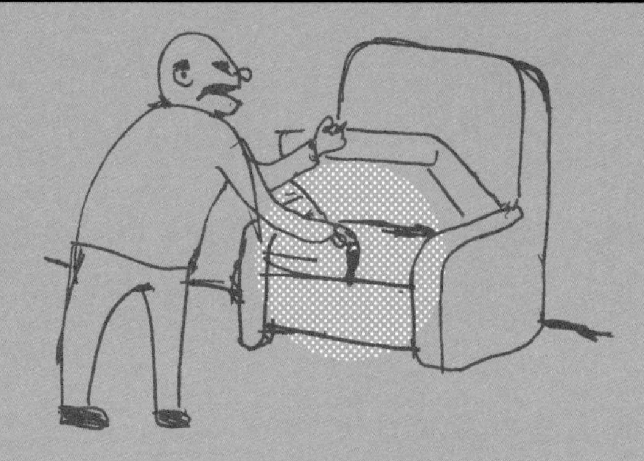

WEDNESDAY
Hide people's car keys so they have to take the bus

SATURDAY
Hang up people's mobile phones for them unless the conversation sounds useful to mankind

SUNDAY
Go to your local airport and scare people out of flying

Monday 14

Tuesday 15

Wednesday 16

Thursday 17

Friday 18

Saturday 19

Sunday 20

Monday 21

Tuesday 22

Wednesday 23

Thursday 24

Friday 25

Saturday 26

Sunday 27

Father Xmas Week!

This week, send anonymous Christmas presents

Traditional Christmas gift-giving is not selfless – you expect a gift in return. Father Christmas alone gives generously, without any notion of reciprocity. This year, emulate his example and spread some anonymous peace and good will.

Dear occupant of
17 Ashfield Rd, Leeds
I don't know if you play tennis, but here's a tennis racquet to get you started. Merry Xmas!

Anon

Dear you,
I picked your letterbox at random. This CD was a "Christmas Staff Pick" at HMV! If you like music, you'll surely enjoy it.
Yours anonymously.
x

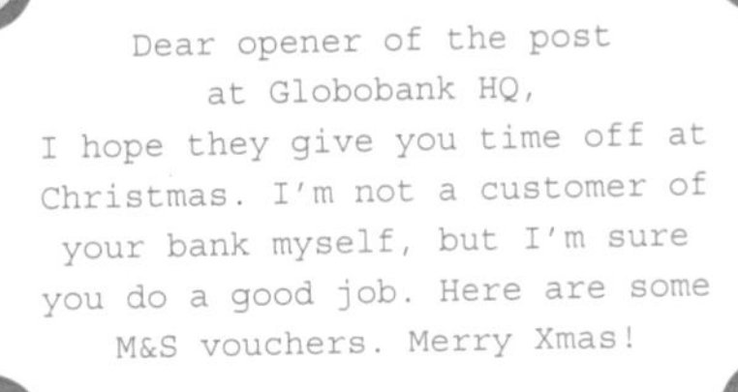

Dear opener of the post
at Globobank HQ,
I hope they give you time off at Christmas. I'm not a customer of your bank myself, but I'm sure you do a good job. Here are some M&S vouchers. Merry Xmas!

Dear
person-I-found-in-the-phone-book,
I liked your name so I decided to
send you this designer ashtray
for Christmas. I hope it comes in
useful!
Me
Dear neighbour
We live on the same street and
yet we've never met. Imagine
that! From what I can see of your
interior, you seem to like books,
so here's one for Christmas.
See you around!
Dear government official at the
Ministry of Justice! As I've
never met you, I simply didn't
know what to buy - but everyone
needs a cheese grater at some
point. Anyway, I hope it comes in
useful. Best wishes for 2010!
A grateful citizen

Monday 28

Tuesday 29

Wednesday 30

Thursday 31

Friday 1

Saturday 2

Sunday 3

Congratulations!

Now that you have been through one year of Benrik's life-changing guidance, you must now be in a position to make your own contribution to history. Contribute your idea for a life-changing task to next year's edition; if it gets in, your name will be famous, like the names of the people on page 174! Send to Benrik, c/o United Agents, 12-26 Lexington Street, London, W1F 0LE, UK.

BENRIK HYMN

The Benrik hymn is a musical statement of Benrik's stance on political issues, written for 1,400 voices. To add your voice to the choir, visit www.benrik.co.uk where you may download a demonstration of the notes to be sung, along with the accompanying guitar track.

You should then send Benrik your own recording of the hymn (as an MP3, AIFF or WAV file). The choir will be assembled in clusters, as shown above, and will eventually be available on the Benrik website.

In collaboration with *H.M.S Cyclones*

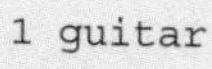

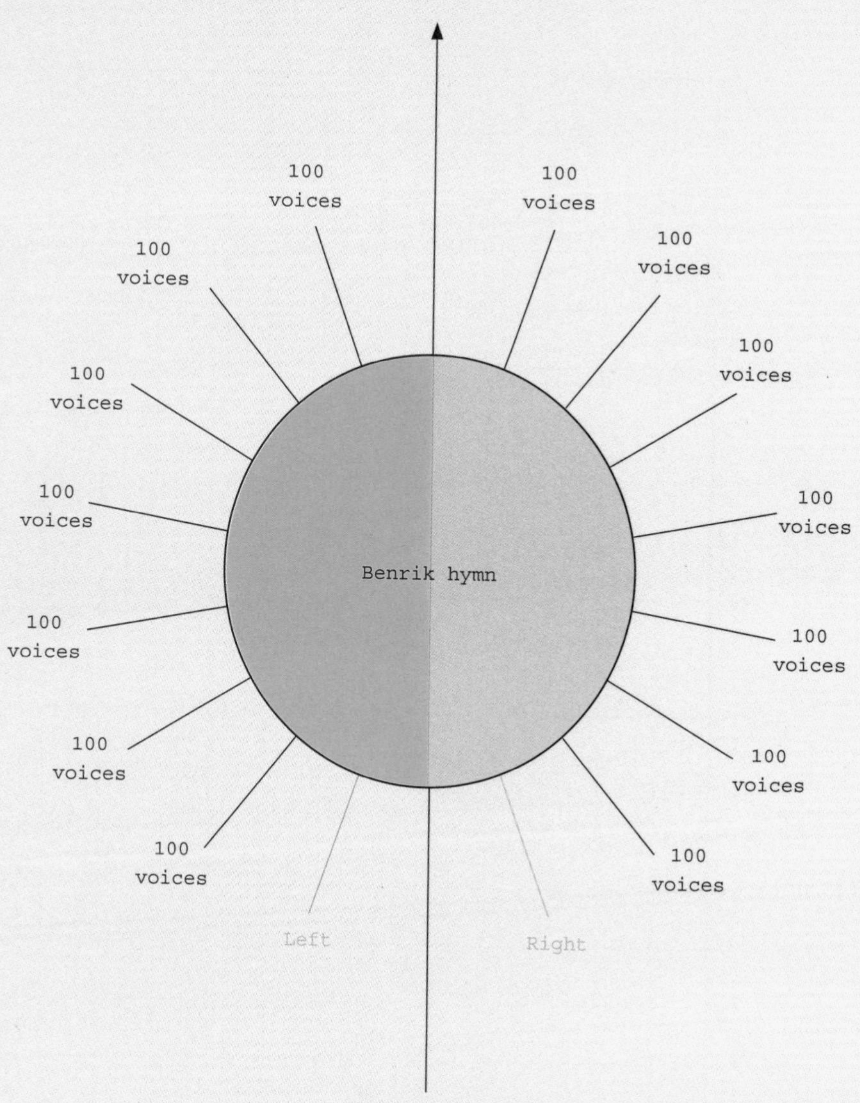

STEREO SPECTRUM

1400 voice choir with classical
guitar accompaniment

Mood Chart

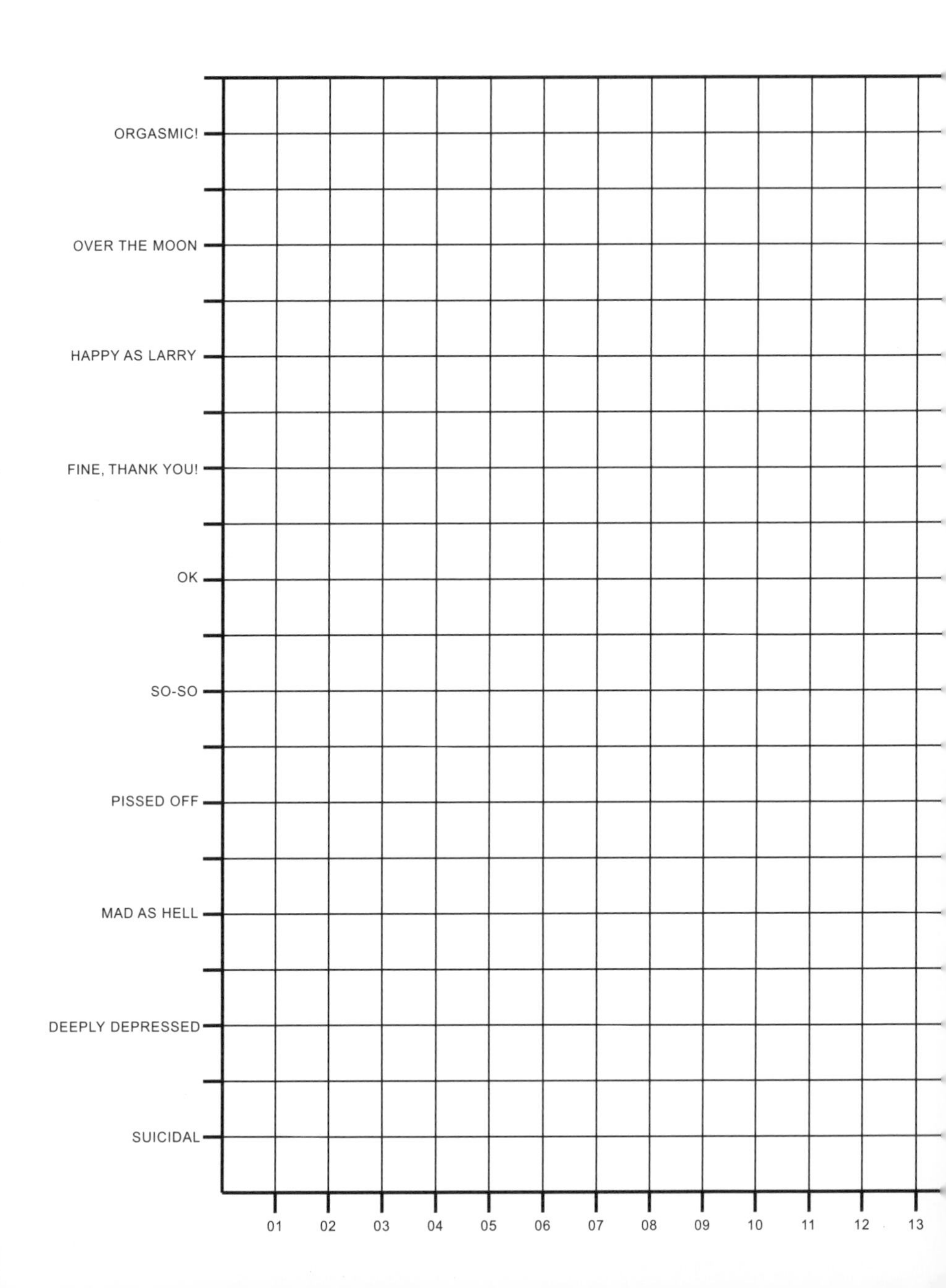

ORGASMIC!
OVER THE MOON
HAPPY AS LARRY
FINE, THANK YOU!
OK
SO-SO
PISSED OFF
MAD AS HELL
DEEPLY DEPRESSED
SUICIDAL
01
02
03
04
05
06
07
08
09
10
11
12
13

Plot mood level every day of the month against vertical axis. Show one year's results to psychotherapist. Check www.benrik.co.uk for the World Mood-Chart

MIND CONTROL

Last year, Benrik tested the compliance of their disciples by tagging them for the week. A few of them appear here. Expect further intrusion into lives as the technology allows it.

Keen? Try our Bonus Tasks!

Today, volunteer for jihad on behalf of the West

World civilizations are clashing! Yet where are the young men and women fighting to defend Western values with their lives? Today, drop everything, book a ticket to the Pakistani badlands, and tell your proud family you're off to join the battle on behalf of Mozart, Shakespeare and Rembrandt.

Today, fight the power

1) Work out who the power is:

- Church .... ☐
- Government.............................. ☐
- Media... ☐
- Corporations.............................. ☐
- Military-industrial complex........... ☐
- Alien mind-control........................ ☐

2) Fight it:

- Victory.. ☐
- Draw.. ☐
- Defeat.. ☐

Birthday Day

Today, tell everyone you meet it's your birthday in order to receive preferential treatment.

- Free haircut at the hairdresser's ☐
- Extra scoop at the ice cream parlour ☐
- Upgrade on the business flight ☐
- Jump the queue at the supermarket ☐
- Lower fine from the parking attendant ☐
- Higher mark from the examiner ☐
- One-day extension on Death Row ☐

Happy birthday!

NB.: Don't follow this task on your actual birthday you gutless individual

Today, listen to music you hate

Guards at Guantanamo use gangsta rap and heavy metal to break down detainees. Increase your resistance to potential psychological torture by subjecting yourself to 24 hours of music you can't normally bear. No cheating: Turn up the volume.

As long as you have completed your task for the week, you may perform these extra free "bonus tasks" at any point in the year.

Test the state's sense of humour today

Dear state,
I am preparing to overthrow you, but I thought I'd give you a chance to surrender beforehand. Let me know.

Name
Address

Send to: 10 Downing St, London SW1

Unwanted Advice Day

- You shouldn't let your child run around like that
- Is that dress not a bit risqué for someone your age?
- Your novel has too many long words in it
- I know a great place to bleach that moustache of yours
- Are you sure those handcuffs are tight enough officer?
- I wouldn't lower the landing gear quite yet if I were you

Leave your doors unlocked today

Trust your fellow citizens for a change

Burgled .... ☐

Not burgled....................................... ☐

Today, help prepare the Earth for our alien guests

The aliens are bound to visit us at some point. We don't want them to find all our anti-alien material when they do, so start getting rid of it now. Examples of anti-alien material to destroy or hide:

- X-files box sets (aliens as threat)
- Alien, Alien 2, Alien 3 (negative portrayal of alien)
- Independence Day (could suggest ideas of invasion)
- E.T. (ridicules the alien)
- Roswell (dissection of aliens)

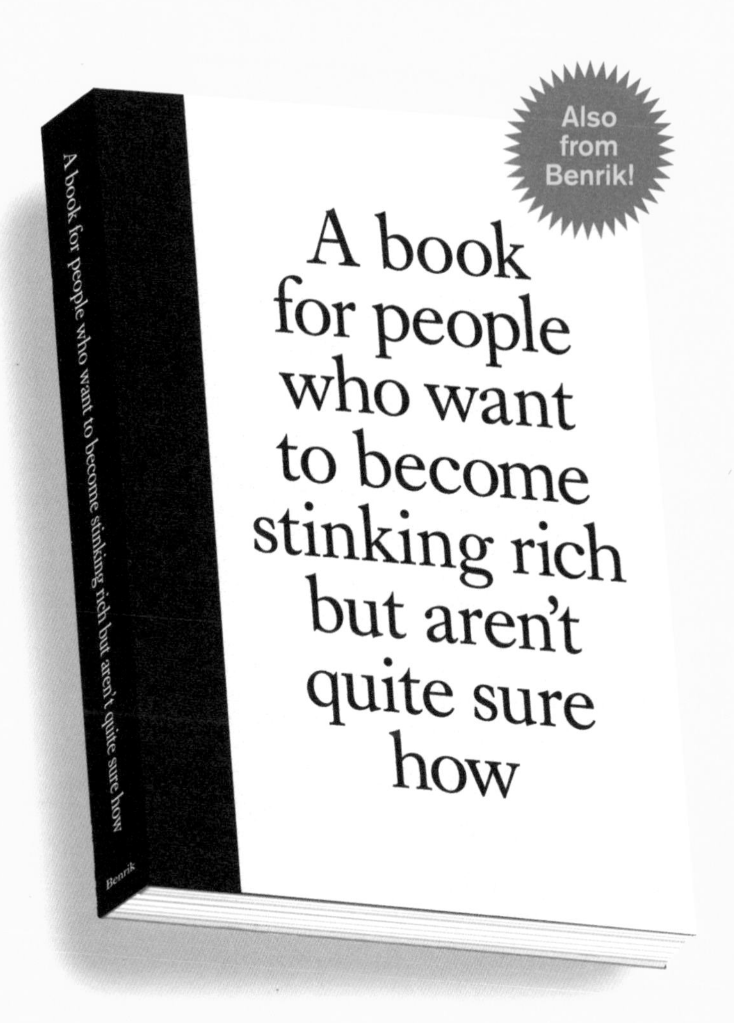

The *Diary* changes you spiritually.
This book will change you materially!
150 ideas to make capitalism more
imaginative, and to make you
obnoxiously rich in the process.

Benrik Ltd are Ben Carey and Henrik Delehag. They were assisted on this project by Claudia Alvear Bello.

Benrik would like to thank the following people for going beyond the call of duty: Kathy Peach, Sarah Bagner, Lana Ivanyukhina, Anton Delehag, Dusty Miller, Simon Trewin, Ariella Feiner, Jon Butler, Bruno Vincent, Richard Milner, Rebecca Ikin, Amy Lines, James Long, Euan Adie, Michael Bhaskar, Sara Lloyd, Richard Hytner, Bernard and Colin David, Robert Saville, Matt Clark and all at Mother, Igor Clark, Iain Tait, Asi Sharabi, Steph Mylam and all at Poke, Ollie Wright, all at Saturday, Moo, Seb Bishop, Hannah Melia, Carol MacArthur, Hayley Newman, Mel Elliott, Lucy Thomas, Andy Moreno, Jon Cooke, Trevor Franklin, Simon Lai, Richard Prue Alex & Elizabeth Carey, Aunt, Katy Follain, Antony Topping, Stefanie, Charlotte, Tommy and Matty Drews, Colin Rowat, Gaby Vinader, Sarah Woodruff, Tom Uhart, Alan Payne, Jan Lyness, Bernard Sue & John Peach, Fredrik Nordbeck, Eva Edsjo, Alex Hutchins, Rina Donnersmarck, Almut, Kenneth & Anna-Lena & Lovisa & Hjalmar & Elin Delehag.

www.thiswebsitewillchangeyourlife.com

All illustrations, photography, design and typography by Benrik, except as follows.
Where the work is not property and copyright of the authors, all attempts have been made by the authors to contact correct copyright holders. The authors would like to gratefully thank for permission to include the following within this edition: Photography weeks 6: Altrendo, 7: Eric Bean / Stone, Hugh Sitton / Photographer's Choice, Jim Cochrane / First Light, Daniel Bosier / Stone, Tim Hall / Taxi, 9: Julio Lopez Saguar / Photonica, 18: Katherine Sfeir / DK Stock , Regine Mahaux / Photographer's Choice, 27: Eric Tucker / Stone+, Mai / Time & Life Pictures, 28: Ebby May / Stone, 33: Clive Streeter / Dorling Kindersley, 35: Three Lions / Hulton Archive, 36: Ed Honowitz / Taxi, Adam Burn / fStop, Image Source, Image Source, Hans Neleman / Photodisc, John Lund/Drew Kelly / Blend Images, 40: Mike Kemp / Rubberball Productions, 43: Christopher Thomas / Photographer's Choice, 45: UpperCut Images, 47: Mel Curtis / Photonica, all © Getty Images; photography week 10 © Mel Elliott; week 16 © Veronica Nordlund; week 28 (group shot) © Benrikians. Photography used under the terms of the Creative Commons Public Licence, which can be found on Flickr: week 2 "Janne Z party - my plate" (Per Ola Wilberg); week 28 "Hotel area" (Matti Mattila). Illustrations week 22 © Lana Ivanyukhina; weeks 19 and 25 © Rina Donnersmarck; week 42 © Lynn. Thanks to all Benrikians photographed on the "Mind Control" page. And thank you to all the Benrik readers who sent in ideas, and in particular to those whose ideas were selected: Week 4 © Gene Sweeney; Week 12 © Wazzawazzawoo; Weeks 13 and 51 © Joel Moss Levinson; Week 18 © Kelly Cobain; Week 19 © Rebecca Wright; Week 28 © Hilary Foote; Week 35 © Julia Connell; Week 42 © Catherine Long; Week 49 © Steven Booth; Week 50 © Yousuf Rangoonwala; Concept of Bonus Days © MariGR; Bonus Day "Listen to music you hate" © Alex Greimann. Official author portraits © Guy Drayton. If there is further enquiry, please contact the authors c/o United Agents, 12-26 Lexington Street, London, W1F 0LE, UK.

First published 2008 by Boxtree
An imprint of Pan Macmillan Ltd
Pan Macmillan, 20 New Wharf Road, London N1 9RR
Basingstoke and Oxford
Associated companies throughout the world
www.panmacmillan.com

ISBN 978-0-7522-2668-2

9 8 7 6 5 4 3 2 1

A CIP catalogue record for this book is available from the British Library

Printed and bound in Italy by Printer Trento

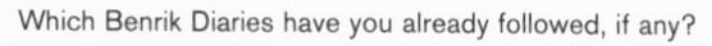

Which Benrik Diaries have you already followed, if any?

2004 ☐

2005 ☐

2006 ☐

2007 ☐

2008 ☐

Note: If you have purchased all of these Diaries and your life has not yet changed, either you are beyond help, or you are not doing it right. Consult experienced Benrik followers on www.thiswebsitewillchangeyourlife.com for guidance.

Your Values Are Our Toilet Paper